SCIENCE IN SCHOOLS

SCIENCE IN SCHOOLS

Proceedings of a Conference under the auspices of

THE BRITISH ASSOCIATION
FOR THE ADVANCEMENT OF SCIENCE

held on April 17th and 18th, 1958, at the
Royal Geographical Society,
London, S.W.7

Edited with Postscript by

W. H. PERKINS, O.B.E.

LONDON
BUTTERWORTHS SCIENTIFIC PUBLICATIONS
1958

A41/728

BUTTERWORTHS PUBLICATIONS LTD.
88 KINGSWAY, LONDON, W.C.2.

AFRICA:	BUTTERWORTH & CO. (AFRICA) LTD. DURBAN: 33/35 Beach Grove
AUSTRALIA:	BUTTERWORTH & CO. (AUSTRALIA) LTD. SYDNEY: 8 O'Connell Street MELBOURNE: 430 Bourke Street BRISBANE: 240 Queen Street
CANADA:	BUTTERWORTH & CO. (CANADA) LTD. TORONTO: 1367 Danforth Avenue
NEW ZEALAND:	BUTTERWORTH & CO. (AUSTRALIA) LTD. WELLINGTON: 49/51 Ballance Street AUCKLAND: 35 High Street

Made and printed in Great Britain by
The Press at Coombelands Ltd., Addlestone, Surrey

FOREWORD

by

Sir Alexander Fleck, K.B.E., F.R.S.

President of the British Association for the Advancement of Science

The British Association for the Advancement of Science is well known for the deliberations at its annual meetings, which each year bring the progress of science to the notice of a wide public—both those particularly in the region of the meeting place and, more generally, those reached by the national press. It is perhaps less well known for its interests in the social and international relations of science. As a result of these and similar activities, the Association became convinced that more attention should be focused on the condition of science teaching in schools.

There have, of course, been discussions elsewhere about the schools and their shortages of staff and equipment, but it seemed timely this spring to hold a general Conference, the proceedings of which are contained in the following pages. I am glad to have the opportunity, as President of the Association, to write an introductory note partly to state my adherence to the claims of urgency, and partly to commend and thank the distinguished speakers who made the Conference so lively. We can now be quite clear that rapid technological change must affect the activities of all our schools, even those for young children. The effects, which will be quickly felt, may be disturbing if they are not prepared for. I notice that one speaker (Miss Huxstep) even suggested that the principles of work study should be applied to the curricula at least of the grammar schools. That may be going rather far, but there is no doubt that adjustment is needed, more rapid than we have hitherto realized. From the vocational point of view we shall have to produce more men and women who are trained to play their part in complex technological processes. The exact number to be so trained may be a matter for argument in present conditions. It is sometimes thought that these newly trained people will become a separate class, unable to communicate with their non-scientific friends and even having difficulty with other scientific specialists. The object of educational change must be to make this argument unnecessary and to carry traditional humanism into a new industrial setting. It seems to me that the Conference has recognized this point, though there are still uncertainties about methods, about degrees of specialization, and about the distribution and rewards of trained ability. I can confirm that it is not only in educational and cultural fields but also in industry that the plight of the schools is evoking much thought and also sympathy from which various forms of practical help are emerging.

I am glad that the proceedings of the Conference are being published so that the ideas expressed may reach a wider circle. I also note that various suggestions for action were made, some of them for action by the British Association. I am sure that these suggestions will be carefully considered and that the Association will maintain its interest in the work of the schools. But the great merit of this publication is that it takes a good step towards making science in schools everybody's problem: it must not remain merely a specialist's dilemma.

ALEXANDER FLECK

CONTENTS

vii

CONTENTS

INTRODUCTION

Sir Ben Lockspeiser

In welcoming you all on behalf of the British Association, I should like to state, very briefly, the two main reasons which led us to invite you here. In the first place, this Conference follows naturally and logically on one which we held some months ago at Leeds. It then emerged that the question of science teaching in schools was basic to our other subject—namely Science in Industry. Secondly, we have been made aware of the concern— if that if not too mild a word—of the Incorporated Association of Head Masters and other educational bodies about the shortage of science teachers and inadequate laboratory accommodation and equipment.

These are, in our view, serious matters, and we are very fortunate indeed that Lord Heyworth has been able to accept our invitation to open our proceedings. He would not have come here unless he was convinced that we had a serious subject on hand, not only for industry but for the country as a whole.

There is no need for me to introduce Lord Heyworth, and no need for me to explain why we welcome him with the greatest pleasure.

OPENING ADDRESS

THE RT. HON. THE LORD HEYWORTH

The British Association have done me the honour of asking me to open this Conference on Science in Schools and I can think of more than one reason why they may have thought it appropriate to invite a representative of industry to perform this task. First, there is the immediate—one might almost say the selfish—interest of industry in seeing that the need for scientists and technologists for its own ranks is satisfied. I need not labour this point, for among the many voices which are raised today in lament over the shortage of scientists, that of industry can be heard shouting with the best. We face a perennial recruitment problem. We send our emissaries out into the highways and the by-ways of the universities in our efforts to compel the scientists to come in. Sometimes, I am afraid, these talent-spotting expeditions distract the young men and women from their studies and are something of an irritation to their tutors, but that is by the way.

It did cross my mind that one reason for inviting me to this Conference was to give me an opportunity of hearing a few home truths. It is sometimes said that if there is a shortage of science teachers in the schools, industry is largely to blame because, with the promise of greater material rewards and more glittering prizes than the scholastic world has to offer, it lures into its own service many who would otherwise have taken up teaching. Through the courtesy of the organizers of the Conference I have been supplied with précis of what the speakers on the programme are going to say, and on glancing through them I am not sure whether this particular point is going to be made against me—or against the President of your Association.

No doubt there is an all-round shortage of scientists for all the jobs that need doing: pure research, applied research and teaching. The present supply does not match the sum total of the demands of the universities, the Government, the schools and industry. But if the finger is pointed particularly at industry, we should perhaps consider whether it is the scientists in industry who are over-paid or the scientists in teaching who are under-paid. We would probably all agree that if a man or woman were to choose teaching as a career solely from considerations of salary, he or she would be unlikely to be an outstanding success. I appreciate, and I admire, the sense of vocation which leads people into the teaching profession and we can be thankful that there are always many who have that sense of vocation. But the question of material rewards cannot be ignored and it would be false delicacy to skate over it as something too crudely commercial for mention. I very much agree with the speaker in whose notes I see the observation that good science teachers cannot be had on the cheap. And I very much disagree with Bernard Shaw's wounding remark that ' he who can, does; and he who can't, teaches.' This seems to me both a silly and a mischievous epigram.

The schools, I suggest, have a two-fold role to play in the teaching of science. First, they have to give the necessary ground-work to those who are going on to the universities, the colleges of technology and similar institutions, there to specialize in some branch of science with a view to making their career in it. But, apart from these specialists, it is increasingly important that every man and woman, whatever he or she intends to do in life, should have a basic background knowledge of the fundamentals of science. I have little doubt that such a background would make the people in my own or any other industrial enterprise considerably more effective in their jobs, even though these may have no immediate connection with the technical or research sides. And on a wider front it is surely desirable that in this present age every citizen should have at least a basic knowledge of science and its problems.

I see that Sir Eric James is going to deal with this subject in some detail and I will not enlarge upon it except to say that the schools have a vital part to play. For although some very interesting pioneer work is being done in this field at such places as the University College of North Staffordshire, the bulk of the rising generation finish their formal education at school. If they are to acquire a background knowledge of science, they must get it at school or nowhere.

It is quite a number of years since I left school and my recollections of how science was taught—or indeed what science

3

was taught—are beginning to grow dim. One thing, however, is certain and that is that there is a great deal more science to learn than when I was a boy. The frontiers of knowledge have advanced at an ever-accelerating pace over the last forty or fifty years and the pace is still quickening. This must constitute a considerable problem for the teachers. They have continually not only to keep their own knowledge up to date but to determine how a quart of knowledge—a continually expanding quart, if there can be such a thing—is to be fitted into the pint-pot of the school curriculum. Perhaps it is some help to them that, as one speaker is going to say, children now begin to acquire their first knowledge of science, and have their interest in it stimulated, younger than ever before. The part played in this process by such adventitious aids as the wireless, television and children's magazines is by no means to be despised.

Before I finish, I would like to congratulate the British Association on having arranged a conference on this most important subject and on having persuaded such a well-chosen list of speakers to take part in it. The problem which they will be discussing can, I think, be reduced to the following essentials. What is the object? To attain that object how many teachers are needed? What sort of teachers? What equipment do they need? Have we got the teachers and have we got the equipment? If not, how do we get them? If you look at the programme for the next two days I think you will see that it is designed to deal with all these points and it is with some relief that I realize that all I have to do is to pose the problems. I can now sit back and wait for the answers to be given by the speakers who will be addressing you today and tomorrow. And do not forget that if, by any chance, the speakers do not come up with the answers, or come up with answers with which you disagree, then in the discussions which follow each session you, ladies and gentlemen in the body of the hall, will have an opportunity of giving the answers yourselves. And I very much hope that you will do so.

SESSION I

SCOPE OF THE CONFERENCE

SIR BEN LOCKSPEISER, CHAIRMAN

Lord Heyworth has clearly established the seriousness of our subject and we are very grateful to him for doing so from his unrivalled knowledge and experience.

The point of view of an outsider on all these matters was recently expressed to me rather pointedly by a foreign colleague of mine. He said: ' I hardly ever pick up any of your scientific and technical journals, going back now for some years, without finding some article or some report on discussions as to how you are going to get more science into your education.' He then said: ' How long is this going on? Is it an interminable matter? ' And he added, with a twinkle in his eye: ' It is rather like your national pastime of cricket.' I replied: ' Since you have mentioned cricket, it gives me an opportunity to say that we have made considerable progress. In the early years of this century a certain head master was pressed by his governors to make provision for some science teaching in his curriculum, and he introduced classes in chemistry on Saturday afternoons as an alternative to cricket.' No one can say that we have not moved on from that situation.

But then, of course, we have had a long way to go. It is for you in this audience to say, but it is my impression that we have still a lot of leeway to make up. The young people are all right —at least I notice that a very large proportion of them still disobey their elders, as they always have done, so the stuff of youth is not changed. But when we consider the kind of age that we live in—an age which, whether we like it or not, is coming more and more under the influence of scientific thought and knowledge, when we remember the young people whom we are expecting to keep the country going in this age, we must ask ourselves: Are we acting fairly by them? Are we giving them the kind of education and training which they ought to be getting?

5

The first thing to do is to get facts, and the object of our discussion is to try and establish the facts by inviting here people who, as a result of experience and study, can speak with the necessary authority.

After they have spoken there will be time for what will, I hope, be lively discussion in which any member of the audience can take part. A verbatim report will be made both of the main speeches and the discussion; it will be edited for publication so that the issues which are raised can be more widely studied. We hope that the publication will take place in time for the Annual Meeting of the Association in August.

In this morning's session, we shall hear from Sir Solly Zuckerman, Sir Eric James and Miss Huxstep. Sir Solly is Chairman of the Scientific Manpower Committee of the Advisory Council on Scientific Policy, and therefore able to speak with unique authority on the national need. Sir Eric is surely better able than anyone else to talk about the status of science in the range of liberal studies; and I know that Miss Huxstep will make us all realize how important are the problems which are presented by the scientific education of girls.

THE NATIONAL NEED

Sir Solly Zuckerman

It gives me great pleasure to be here today. Among you I recognize many who are in closer touch than I am with the problem I have to discuss; I have certainly learnt many of my facts from people whom I see in front of me. On the other hand, if we are to do what Lord Heyworth has suggested—namely, to specify our object before we seek to find out whether or not we have the people to attain it—I can help by summarizing briefly for you some of the relevant statistics.

I have been asked to speak on the question of the national need. Sir Ben has already told us that a friend of his from the Continent has suggested that discussion of this question has become just another national pastime. The truth is that our national need is also an international need. We are not alone in talking about the problem; we are discussing a phase of transformation which affects the world as a whole.

The need for scientists, and the need to increase the volume of scientific education and the output of the schools, applies to all countries, and certainly to those of the Western Alliance. It has recently been recognized by the establishment of a Science Committee of NATO. The theme of the present discussion may very likely dominate the deliberations of the NATO Committee, in the same way as it already does the deliberations of the corresponding committee of OEEC. We in Great Britain were probably the first of the Western countries to recognize that the problem existed. We have known for some considerable time that we have to provide not only industry, not only the schools, but also the Government machine with more and more people trained to deal with the facts of a world which is being rapidly transformed by scientific and technical advances. Our society cannot for long consist of one section aware of the nature of this transformation, and another which does not understand the forces of knowledge which are at work. It is the elimination of this dichotomy

7

in our society with which, I am happy to see, this Conference is mainly concerned. Sir Eric James, who will speak on Science as a Component of General Education, has put his finger on a critical problem in meeting the national need.

I have said that we in this country were slightly more advanced than others in recognizing the problem. When the second world war began it was immediately realized that our educational system had not provided enough people competent to deal at all levels with the new apparatus of war. A crash-programme of technical education had to be instituted. Before the war ended, officials and others had started to calculate what the costs of reconstruction would be. Their calculations were not made just in terms of money and steel, they also looked at technical man-power. Then, in 1945, the Government of the day set up a com-mittee (the Barlow Committee, as it became called), which tried to estimate, with very limited statistical material at its disposal, the national need for scientists.

The Report of the Barlow Committee did not attempt to prophesy the trend of events in precise numerical terms. Its aim was to set up a target for action, its main recommendation being that resources should be provided to allow the universities to double their output as quickly as possible. That task took only about four years.

The period from the end of the war up to about 1950 or 1951 represented what I have always regarded as the first phase in the expansion of higher and technical education in this country. Then began the second phase. The moment we were caught up in the Korean War it became apparent that what we had achieved was insufficient—the demand for scientific manpower could not be satisfied. So a further assessment of the need was made, which was translated into action again by the Government of the day, in plans to extend facilities for education in new directions, to enlarge universities further in certain specialized departments, to build up the technical colleges, and so on.

The third phase is, in a sense, the one which is now beginning. Again, merely for convenience, it is useful to see it in terms of an assessment which the Committee on Scientific Manpower arrived at after studying output, requirements and demand. On this occasion we started with slightly more precise figures than

8

those which were available to Sir Alan Barlow's Committee. The Ministry of Labour carried out a survey of the number of qualified scientists and engineers in the country. That provided us, for the first time, with a fairly good indication—although certainly not as precise as we should have wished—of the actual number of professional scientists and engineers in the country. We knew where those people were, we knew in what industries they were, and we knew how they were distributed—between industry and public service in the Government departments, between schools, universities and technical colleges. By making certain assumptions about the likely growth in demand we projected these figures into the future.

I should say a word about our assumptions. So far as the demand from industry is concerned, it can be taken as a general fact that a relationship exists between the amount that industry invests in scientific manpower and the growth of its output. People have tried to calculate the relation in various ways. We did so by the simple device of writing to people like Lord Heyworth and others and finding out what they thought about future needs, and about the relation of the output of their companies to the size of their technical staffs. We ended up with a rather simple numerical relationship. On the average, it turned out that you have to double the numbers of scientific professional manpower employed in order to double output. That proposition has not yet been challenged; but it is obviously no more than a provisional estimate.

I must make it clear that this one-to-one proportion applies to industry as a whole; and that it may vary widely over the industrial range. But it does represent a rough guide and index. It is the best measure we have at the moment; and it is certainly as good as any yet provided in any other country.

Our second assumption, or rather 'condition,' concerned the growth of the national product in this country. Of course, nobody can exactly predict by how much the national product is going to increase from year to year. But we can study the data over a period of years and set a target which is reasonable if you assume a healthy growth of the economy. We ultimately assumed an average increase for industry as a whole of about 4 per cent per annum. Since the chemical industry and the engineering industry

9

B

are growing at a very much more rapid rate, whereas other industries are growing more slowly, it is necessary to emphasize that 4 per cent is a weighted average for the whole of industry. Once the figure was agreed, and accepting the one-to-one ratio I have already referred to, it was possible to calculate the rest. The answer was that we had to double the output of professional scientists and engineers by the end of the 1960's. We were impressed by the extent of the effort which would be needed to provide for what some people regarded as not very pressing demands of industry over the years ahead.

This was our ' overall ' answer. It took into account what was likely to happen in the field of public employment, in the schools and the universities. In the case of the schools we were not able, of course, to predict what future Government policy was likely to be. We knew that the aim of the Ministry of Education is to improve the educational facilities in all schools, and to reduce the size of classes. We knew that progress to this goal is rather slow, and that many more teachers—including scientists—would be needed. We were able to make certain inspired guesses about public departments, knowing that in general the Government cannot be very lavish about letting departments employ all the scientists they want in a period of scarcity when salaries are rising. Ultimately we assumed that economy in some sectors of public employment would be counterbalanced by increasing demand in others. Those assumptions were arbitrary, but they led us to define the objective for which we are striving at the present moment—to double the annual output of professional scientists and engineers between 1955/6 and the end of the 1960's.

Let me say straight away that neither any member of the Scientific Manpower Committee nor the officials who assist that Committee, nor the authorities in industry whom we consulted, nor the Advisory Council to which the Committee reports, will be the least bit surprised if our goal is achieved sooner than 1970; we shall be very disappointed if it takes longer to achieve. Equally, we shall not be surprised if the demand for scientific manpower proves greater than we estimated. We shall, however, be surprised and sorry if it proves to be less. If it does, the main reason is likely to be that the economy is not growing at the rate for which we were estimating.

The target set by my Committee has been accepted, and the effort to produce the required number of people is now well under way. In effect, what is being attempted is to increase the university entry by one-third of its present amount in ten years. That is a formidable task, bearing in mind the present strain on the universities.

I do not wish to weary you with figures, but I suppose that I ought to mention a few more so that you may set a numerical frame to the problem in which you are all involved much more closely than I am. The number of graduates in the basic and engineering sciences turned out by the universities in 1939 was 3,000. The first post-war crop was nearly double—5,600. Four years later it had risen to 7,000. It then fell somewhat but by 1956/7 it had again passed 7,000.

To these numbers we must add those who, after spending some time in a technical college, obtain a qualification equivalent to a university degree—for instance, membership of one of the professional institutions. We know very little about the pre-war figures for this group, but the 1956 figures added to the number of university graduates bring the output of professional scientists and engineers in that year to about 12,000. That was a substantial increase on 1955. We have not yet got the figure for 1957, but we can be fairly certain that it is well above 12,000. So if our target is to be reached we must, in the next ten years or so, gradually increase our annual output from 12,500 to 20,000.

It seems as if this task is going to be divided nearly equally between the universities and the technical colleges. If it is so shared, the technical colleges will have to do what was suggested in 1956 by the Government's White Paper on Technical Education —otherwise the pressure on the universities is likely to be greater than they can sustain on present showing. But present trends make me optimistic. I think that the technical college output will reach the heights set for it, and in the same way I am hopeful that the universities, aided as they will be by the new generous Treasury grants, will also be able to do their share.

The numbers of students who have been taking up the basic and engineering sciences in the universities since 1953 have been increasing at the rate of 10 per cent a year, and entries for the current academic year are nearly 50 per cent higher than they were five years ago—10,800 as compared with 7,300. If this trend continues we shall get the output figures that were set by the Scientific Manpower Committee, and which have been accepted as a basis of Government policy. In fact, the Chancellor of the Exchequer has intimated that we might even see those figures being surpassed before the end of the 1960's. We must be careful, however, lest the sharp increase in output in the next two or three years makes people say: 'Are we not overdoing all this scientific education? ' and lest this leads to relaxation of effort.

I should now like, with some hesitation, to consider the relationship of the flow through the universities with that through the schools. The university population at the end of the 1960's will number somewhere between 124,000 and 135,000. That means an annual entry of anything from 35,000 to 38,000, including a certain number—estimated at about 3,000—from overseas.

We may assume, in accordance with the Government's White Paper on Technical Education, that the technical college entry over the same period is likely to rise to about 23,000, of which something like one-half will come from the sixth forms. Nearly all the 35,000 to 38,000 to be admitted by the universities will be sixth formers. If, in addition, we assume an increase in the period of teachers' training, but no significant increase in the total size of the training colleges by the late 1960's, they will be requiring each year 10,500 people who will also come from the sixth forms.

When all necessary allowances are made, we can estimate that by 1967/8—ten years hence—something like 53,000 to 56,000 of the intake into what I will call higher education—the universities, the teachers' training colleges and the technical colleges—will be the product of the sixth forms. This will not be the entire intake, of course, since the technical colleges provide a means of bringing forward those people who have not gone through the sixth form but have continued their higher education after leaving school. The figure of about 55,000 compares with something like 37,000 today.

In 1955/6 the sixth-form population was 61,000 out of a total 17-year-old age group of 651,000, that is 9·4 per cent. The figures for January, 1957, were 63,000 out of 645,000—nearly 10 per cent. The age group is expected to reach the level of 930,000 in 1964/5 —as a result of the post-war increase in births—before it starts to decline again in 1965/6, reaching its minimum, about 730,000, in 1968/9, when it starts rising again.

If the trend to later leaving continues at its present rate, the sixth-form population will be 110,000 in 1967/8—about 15 per cent of its age group. About half of this output can be expected to carry on full-time education after the sixth-form stage. The corresponding figure today is 60 per cent. At first glance, therefore, it would seem that the schools will easily be able to cater for the three streams of higher education—the universities, the technical colleges and teachers' training colleges.

Since the universities are not likely to expand at the same rate it also follows that there will be some people who fail to achieve the university education to which they may have been looking forward during their later school days. It also means that the universities will be able, as it were, to reduce the length of the 'tail' of the university entry so that the average undergraduate quality is likely to rise. All this means that we shall be able to set higher standards both in schools and universities.

If we take into account not only the university entry but also those who enter teachers' training colleges and technical colleges within the next ten years, it follows that the fraction of each age group proceeding to a higher education—which was 8 per cent in 1955/6—will be not much greater than 7 per cent at the peak of the bulge, and will rise to 9 per cent at the end of the decade. In relative terms, this is not a very great change. In fact, anybody can calculate from the figures which are already available, that whereas 3·5 per cent of each age group now achieves a university education, that figure, under present plans, cannot exceed 4·4 per cent during the 1960's. It may be much the same as it is today. So, although the absolute number will increase considerably, the proportion of each age group getting a higher education will not be greatly affected.

I have been focusing my remarks on the professionally-trained scientist and engineer. We must remember, however, that countless numbers of sub-professional people will also be required. They are usually referred to as 'technicians,' those whose task it is to follow up the technologists. By whatever name they are called, they are going to be required in far larger numbers, and they must be produced at a rate which increases more rapidly than it has been increasing in recent years.

We are not working under any central control. We are all pushing ahead towards the same goal, and we must hope that difficulties will be sorted out through the interplay of the usual empirical forces on which we always rely in this country, that the sixth forms will grow at the rate required by the technical colleges and universities, that the universities will be able to accept those people who are coming up from schools and who will be counting on a university education; that the technical colleges will develop as they are at present, carrying on with their enormous up-grading process, so that they become not second-rank universities, but institutions of dignity and prestige to which it is as great a privilege to belong as it is to go to a university.

I am sure that all these things will come to pass. The difficulties are not insuperable, provided that we keep our goal in sight, and provided sufficient resources are made available.

SCIENCE AS A COMPONENT OF GENERAL EDUCATION

SIR ERIC JAMES

In introducing the topic of Science in General Education, particularly to this audience, I can scarcely expect to say much that is new. My duty will be rather to be as brief as possible, and to try to stimulate a fruitful discussion of what is increasingly realized to be one of the most important educational questions of our time.

In the first place I think we must remind ourselves how recent is the whole structure of scientific education in our schools. It is, after all, only 100 years since a head master of Winchester, speaking before the Clarendon Commission, could say that, while he might contemplate lectures on nature study, the systematic study of chemistry was not to be thought of. In the century since that was said we have made really remarkable advances, and in a conference of this kind, which is, I suppose, called together so that we should not be complacent, it is nevertheless a good thing that we should remind ourselves how far and how fast we have come. To the statistics that Sir Solly gave us I should like to add one more. The fact that this country produces more graduates in science and technology per thousand of population than any other in Western Europe is one that is too often forgotten. It is a fact which reflects very creditably indeed upon the schools and universities. In spite of all our difficulties, about which we shall rightly hear a good deal during the course of this Conference, the standard of specialist science teaching over the last thirty or forty years has risen very markedly indeed. That improvement has been due to many people, not least to the teachers themselves, working through the Science Masters' Association, and to the Inspectorate.

It is important, too, that we should remember how much thought and experiment is being devoted to the non-scientific education of the science specialist. When we talk about over-specialization it is customary almost always to think of scientists. We still, to some extent, live in an educational climate in which

15

eleven periods a week of Latin from the age of eight is called a broad general education, and three periods a week of science from the age of eleven is called being in danger of premature specialization. We have certainly devoted much more thought to the non-scientific education of the scientist than we have to the converse process, and in view of the rise in the number of such specialists, a number that comprises nearly two-thirds of our sixth forms, in view of the responsibility that those people will increasingly bear, not only as research workers but as administrators and managers, I think that it is right that the general education of scientists should be one of our major preoccupations.

But the view that science is, of its nature, specialized, while everything else is, of its nature, broad and humanizing is really no longer tenable in the modern world. It is no longer tenable because we are realizing that science can be the core of a true and deep education, in the sense that many people will derive their greatest spiritual illumination from the pursuit of scientific truth. This is a world in which, quite obviously, science has much more than a utilitarian value; in which it makes its impact not only on the amenities of life, on economics, on commerce and industry, but on politics and on our very modes of thought. We are driven to recognize the plain fact that no education can now be considered complete which does not include some element of science in the same way that it includes an element of history, of English, and of mathematics.

Everyone will agree with that; it is, I fear, a platitude. But like so many platitudes it is easier to enunciate than to translate into hard practice. For in all problems which affect the curriculum we must try to be much more realistic than we sometimes are, and realize exactly what we are asking in terms of available time. I often feel that a new law of conservation should be enunciated, the law of the conservation of the curriculum. Put in its simplest form, that law states that for everything that you put into the timetable you must throw something out. In particular I would bring that law to the notice of the *Times Educational Supplement*, for, great as is my admiration for that paper, it becomes less than realistic as soon as it devotes itself to the sixth-form curriculum. If we agree that science must be introduced at any particular stage, we must be prepared to state quite clearly what must go out.

At this point we touch the very difficult problems of specialization. In all our thinking about them I feel that we must recognize quite frankly that a considerable degree of specialization in our sixth forms, whether in arts or science is both justified and necessary. It is justified because it is educationally desirable for a boy or girl to have the opportunity of going to some depth in some chosen subjects, and realizing the satisfaction of meeting difficult ideas and techniques. It is necessary because without a high standard in our sixth forms we shall have to prolong considerably our university courses. We have heard Sir Solly speak of the pressures that the ' bulge ' and the ' trend ' are going to put upon our universities. Can we seriously contemplate at the same time prolonging our university courses to five or six years? Yet such a prolongation would be an inevitable result of a dilution of our sixth form standards, whether in the name of general education or for other reasons.

When we assert that no education is complete unless it contains an element of science, we are faced with a second problem. What do we mean by ' science ' ? Non-scientists often speak as though science were a single, limited and defined activity. They forget the enormous area that the word covers. It is today only too easy to take a degree in science, and hence be classed as a ' scientist,' and yet know practically nothing of what is going on in fields of science away from one's own. We cannot speak of science as a single entity: it is, rather, a great constellation of studies, and one that is expanding at an ever-increasing rate. It is in the attempt to meet this difficulty that we devise courses in the ' philosophy of science ' or try to show people ' how a scientist's mind works,' but we must beware that in doing so we do not impose an artificial unity.

Even with these two major difficulties in mind, the difficulty of finding time and the difficulty of definition, the first step in making science part of general education is, of course, reasonably clear. Whatever our more ambitious and fundamental plans, we must at any rate give to all pupils a reasonable grasp of the grammar of the main branches of science. That is necessary whatever one seeks to do afterwards. Scientific method cannot be discussed in a vacuum; the history of science has little significance unless we know something of the elementary facts behind the

17

history. In practical terms, this means that curricula should be so arranged that all suitable pupils, whatever their future specialization, can have a four- or five-year course of chemistry, physics and biology. This is an ideal to which we are moving fairly fast, and it is, indeed, only in one or two of the very best schools that a boy can survive without ever studying any science at all! But it is important that all schools should attempt so to arrange their curricula that no choice between science and 'arts' has to be made before the 'O' level. It is *early* specialization rather than *over*-specialization that is the greatest danger.

Over the next stage there is much more controversy and much more difficulty. Is this four- or five-year course enough, if we give it to everyone? Should we continue some science into the sixth form, or into other further education, for all pupils? If so, what should it be?

My own view is that there must be some such continuation. Some schools and even some universities have, of course, been experimenting with such advanced courses for a considerable time. But in general we are too prone to drop science for our non-scientists at the very stage when they are developing the mental equipment to see its social implications and to relate it to the rest of knowledge. We lay the foundations and put nothing on top, a procedure that is all too common in other fields of education. Just as the scientist can be left with little snippets of Latin that are supposed to represent the classical contribution to civilization, so we must beware lest our non-scientist's view of science rests on the impression that litmus does something when something is added to it.

We are, therefore, faced quite definitely with the problem of devising a course of science appropriate to the 16—18 level. As those of us who have tried to do it know, this is much more difficult than is often supposed. Let us consider the various solutions that have been proposed, and of which some are being tried. First, there are those who, like the *Times Educational Supplement,* deplore teaching arts students *about science,* and wish to teach them *science.* What this means in practice, in so far as it means anything at all, is that historians in the sixth form will study, say, Advanced level physics. Those who support this view, and they incidentally are usually not scientists themselves, maintain that the rigorous study of one science will enable the arts man really to understand the scientist's modes of thought. He will have been subjected to the same discipline as the scientist, and hence will see how his mind ticks. Obviously there is something to be said for this line of thought. It is in my opinion, however, unsatisfactory for several reasons.

First, underlying it is the heresy that scientists and non-scientists think in quite different ways, that there is some peculiar scientific method of thought, and that this is transmissible to the non-scientist by forcing him into a laboratory and giving him a magnetometer or some similar instrument. I do not myself believe that in practice there is this gulf between the scientist and the non-scientist. I believe that in essence the same creative process is at work in the potential scientist as in the potential historian, and that the idea of the automatic educational value of the unrelated 'A' level subject emphasizes rather than bridges this gulf. I think that it may also be justifiably maintained that such a course of study as 'A' level physics for the historian narrows unduly the field of scientific interest. One branch of science alone is touched, and the other great areas remain outside and untouched. Thirdly, I believe that a great deal of the 'A' level course in a major science would be too detailed, too difficult and too dull for the non-scientists. Let us be frank about this. Those of us who are scientists did not find it dull, because science was ultimately the thing that we liked doing more than anything else, and because we knew that we were getting somewhere. In our chosen job we will put up with difficulty and dullness. The non-scientists will not be as receptive. We must face the fact that these people with their interests centred elsewhere, in history or classics or wherever it may be, must be won over to realize the excitements of science, just as the scientist must be won over to appreciate, shall we say, the ' surge and thunder of the Odyssey.' We shall not, in my opinion, succeed with either group by putting them through the specialist course appropriate to future professionals.

Does the history of science, then, provide the answer? This is in many ways an attractive solution, and with the extremely gifted teacher I believe it is one than can work. But in fact, of course, there are few very gifted teachers, and as usually taught

—certainly as it *would* be usually taught if there were more of it—the history of science will not be effective. Even if the knowledge of the grammar of science is adequate, much of the history seems pointless, certainly at the school level, for the following reason. The answers to the problems with which the early scientists were faced are now known even to the non-scientist, for he has some superficial knowledge of the right answers from periodicals and books. He knows, in fact, that the phlogiston theory is wrong, and that burning substances combine with oxygen. To any but the most unsophisticated minds on the one hand or the most sophisticated on the other it seems unreal and pointless to unravel the complex arguments by which the original theory was disproved. In this the history of science differs from that of other ideas— e.g. in philosophy. One can still read Plato with immense satisfaction, because what Plato said about justice has not been entirely superseded; it cannot be *proved* to be right or wrong, and remains a stimulating discussion of a living issue. Such a discussion can never be entirely out of date, even to professional philosophers. By contrast, scientific ideas can often be shown to be clearly wrong, and an air of unreality clouds the retracing of the steps in that demonstration.

Is the solution to our problem of the education of our non-scientists to be found, then, in a study of the philosophy of science or of scientific method? Perhaps, once again, if superbly taught. But here we are approaching matters so difficult that they are better left to the university. The philosophy of science, in so far as the phrase has meaning, happens to be a very difficult kind of philosophy. It is not nearly as attractive to the non-specialist as ethics or politics. Nor is the ' method of science ' a simple idea. It is one of which we speak freely enough, but I wonder how many of us in this room could really give a definition that would not be equally applicable to the methods of historians or classical scholars or some artists? The whole subject is complicated by the frequency with which scientists depend upon illogical and intuitive steps and even on the exploitation of mistakes which have turned out to be fortunate in their results. But a combination of the history and the methodology of science can form a stimulating basis for part of non-specialist teaching. The case-study method has been used by some writers in this field, and

I can recommend two recent volumes by Dr J. B. Conant, *Case Histories in Experimental Science* published by Harvard University Press. Here great ideas in science are analysed in detail, with full quotations from the original papers, and I can imagine a study of them being of great stimulus to some non-scientists.

My own view is that we must seek a solution by attempting to combine the teaching *of* science with teaching *about* science. I have great hopes from the experiments that are being carried out by the selection of one or two vital scientific concepts followed by a study of their development and their consequences. I think that it is best to illustrate the experimental method through one or two practical exercises carried out by the student himself and closely linked with his everyday observations, the kind of work that is being done with great success at Keele by Professor Vick, and at Princeton.

But there must also be a descriptive account of scientific discovery in various fields given in a much less rigorous way, for after all, the student's own specialism will give him training in rigorous thought. We have to build on our elementary factual foundations a structure that will emphasize the effects of science on society and on the general climate of thought. Necessarily this will be superficial, but here, as in other fields of general education, not least in the general education of scientists themselves, we must not be too afraid of the superficial and the popular. Our general aim must be to produce people who have a certain sympathy with what scientists are trying to do, some knowledge as to what science has achieved and may achieve in the future, and ability to converse with scientists, to cross that barrier which is, in fact, so much lower than is often supposed. In all general education we must aim first at a certain basic knowledge, and secondly at the stimulus which together make it possible to read for oneself and to communicate with specialists.

The whole problem is beset by two major difficulties. The first we shall surmount in time; it is simply ignorance of what we should be trying to do, and of how to accomplish it. We shall go on pegging away and sharing our knowledge as teachers have learned to do. The second difficulty will be harder to overcome. The most important limiting factor in this as in all kinds of education, is the quality of the individual teacher. It happens that the kind of work that we have been discussing is unusually difficult, however we tackle it, for to hold the interest of impatient and growing minds in something that is outside their major interest is always difficult. To teach science, this activity of the human spirit, to which so many of us are devoted, and to make it a significant part of general education, without diluting it so that it is unrecognizable, is an immense task. I believe that it is one that is supremely necessary and rewarding, not only so that our pupils may take their place in the world and understand what is going on around them, but so that they may understand more clearly than perhaps they have done in the past the excitements and glories that are part of science's own particular spiritual worth.

SCIENTIFIC EDUCATION FOR GIRLS

Miss E. M. Huxstep

The fact that my subject, Scientific Education for Girls, has been given in this Conference a separate place all to itself, seems to imply that scientific education for girls is either a different kind of thing from science education for everybody else, or that it presents particular problems. The implication that scientific education for girls is of a different nature, or even ought to have a different bias from that of boys, can, I think, be quickly dismissed. There was a time, not so very long ago, when the education of girls aroused some confusion in the minds of those responsible for it. Are girls, we asked ourselves, not by nature different from boys and are they not going to do a wholly different kind of job in life? Are we right, therefore, to be developing girls' education on such closely similar lines to the education of boys? But the tide of history, strongly reinforced by two world wars, has carried us forward to a clearer view. And now in its economic need the nation turns, not for the first time, to women, and invites—nay urges, them to enter every sphere of industry and the professions.

So I am starting from the premise that it is now already accepted that there is no essential difference between girls and boys in mental make-up and no essential difference in the kind of employment they are going into. In a scientific age what implications has this for the education of girls? May we first take a look at the present education pattern for girls, particularly in its scientific content.

What sort of science is taught in girls' schools? How much of it? To whom? By whom? In going on to attempt some answer to these questions, I must first point out two limitations to my survey.

I shall speak of what happens in grammar schools. For girls this definition is taken to include independent, public, direct-grant and aided schools, day and boarding schools as well as maintained schools; for in the girls' system of grammar school education there are no fundamental or essential differences between these schools in

23

their patterns of learning, and what I have to say is equally applicable to them all. I shall speak of grammar schools because I know them best and because what goes on in them presents a fairly coherent and easily defined picture. But if we were to assume that such limitations and difficulties as are present in the girls' grammar schools throughout the country are present in an even more acute form in other kinds of girls' secondary schools, we should not, I think, be wrong.

The second reservation I must make is that the facts I give are not, of course, precisely accurate for every school. Hardly two girls' grammar schools anywhere are exactly alike, in science or in anything else—there is considerable variation of pattern among them. Broadly speaking, however, the picture which follows is a typical one and individual variations from it do not invalidate its general truth.

Let us then assume that there are three broad groups of study with which class teaching is directly concerned at all stages—the humanities, the aesthetic subjects, and the science subjects (in which all the time I include mathematics). I am, of course, aware that there is a good deal of overlap both in the nature of subjects themselves and in their treatment by those who teach them; but I hope I may use this as a broad classification for the sake of assessing the position.

It will also be broadly true that the five, six, seven or eight years of grammar school education fall for most girls in most schools into three fairly well-defined stages: the first three years, from 11 plus to 14 plus, when, on the whole, all girls are following pretty nearly the same curriculum; the next two years, from 14 plus to 16 plus, when some choice between alternatives will have to be made, and some bias will therefore appear; and the last one, two or three years of advanced study in the sixth form, when most of the girls will be committed to a limited group of subjects which is likely to be, (though in almost all girls' schools there is provision otherwise), chosen from within one of the three broad groups of study.

How at each stage does the science group of studies fare as compared with the other two groups? There are obviously two important bases to this comparison—quality and quantity. For the moment I want to look only at quantity for I have something to say about quality in a later connection. As far then as quantity is

24

concerned, during the first stage, 11 plus to 14 plus, the humanities occupy approximately 50 per cent of class time; the aesthetic subjects approximately 25 per cent and sciences (including mathematics) approximately 25 per cent. The science will be a broad course of general elementary science.

During the second stage, 14 plus to 16 plus, the humanities retain approximately 50 per cent of time for almost all the girls—more for some. The other two groups alter their proportions for different groups of girls. Science may dwindle to 20 per cent for some girls and may become wholly biological. For others—generally for the most able—it may increase to 36 per cent. But it certainly will not increase to 36 per cent for a large proportion of girls—seldom for as many as 50 per cent, often for less than 25 per cent. It may continue to be general science or it may be divided into the three separate sciences. If it is so divided it is likely again to be only a comparatively small proportion of girls who carry all three sciences and mathematics to a successful separate standard at Ordinary level.

In the sixth form—and we shall here remind ourselves that by now more than half the girls have left school—the majority will choose among the humanities for their advanced courses; that majority will usually be large—often double the number following science courses; and for that majority there is very seldom indeed any provision for continued science education in the sixth form beyond what has been done in the main school.

That, then, in broad outline is the picture. Obviously, there is a serious ' unbalance ' which ought to be redressed. The redressing must begin in the main school (as far as mathematics is concerned even earlier than that), for it is primarily upon the confident knowledge and enjoyment of a subject in the main school that at 16 plus a girl chooses her sixth form specialism which in turn makes possible certain kinds of careers. Every subject of study, be it languages, sciences, music or swimming, passes through similar stages of learning—the first exciting introduction, the getting down to the inevitable drudgery, and then out on the other side to the beginnings of mastery and of a mature realization of what it is all about. If we are to give all our girls a full and equal choice of specialisms, whether they pursue their specialism at school or in further education, we must see to it that most of the main studies

25

C

reach approximately the same stage by 16 plus and that every girl has had enough of each kind of intellectual discipline to make a soundly based choice. If we are then to be confident that a proper proportion of them will choose science and through a genuine interest in science make for scientific careers; and if we are to make sure that those who do not so choose are not only well-grounded in the basic knowledge and rudimentary techniques of science but as budding linguists, historians, musicians, etc., and as future secretaries, teachers and, above all else, as future citizens continue gladly and profitably in the sixth form a further study of science as part of a general cultural course—then there are two pretty formidable difficulties to be faced: first, the quantity of science teaching in the main school must be increased; and, secondly, the quality of science teaching must be vastly improved both in the main school and in the sixth form. Both these improvements must come first in the main school for many girls will go no further; and for all girls tastes and interests are first formed there and what is done there largely determines what follows in the sixth form and later.

Then quantity first. An increase of quantity obviously means two things—more time and more teachers. You can get more time only, as Sir Eric so clearly emphasized, by taking it from somewhere else. In my view, the aesthetic group of studies already has as little time as it can do with, for this group has its own vital contribution to make to the wholeness of education and perhaps a particular part to play for good living in a mechanistic age. So let us face the issue; the extra time for science has probably got to come from the humanities. From which of them? Before we make our choice let us remind ourselves of one thing: We are seeking a balance, not a different unbalance by putting difficulties in the way of those girls who must and ought to choose different disciplines from those of science; and until pupils are 16 plus, in girls' schools, we do not know and nor, for the most part, do they, which they are going to choose. Where, then, shall we get our time for science?

From English? But already there is complaint of the illiteracy of scientists. What of the girl from the unliterate, inarticulate home who is now in our grammar schools in her hundreds—yes, and in our independent and direct-grant schools too, for money and literacy are no longer synonymous.

From classics? Then you must remove from all universities the qualification of Latin in any shape or form at any level for admission to any honours school whatsoever. It has already gone from some universities for some faculties and some schools. But as long as any desirable university requires it, it will have to be taught. For some of us there may be heart-searching on another point. Suppose that we have removed it altogether as a qualification for university, do we wish to lose the fundamental influence of this study on the English of those girls who have rare gifts in English, gifts of speech or writing; and do we wish to close the doors to the first-hand study of classical literature and thought to all except those who come from homes where the knowledge and love of a subject does not depend on what is taught in schools? In grammar schools of all kinds today we work with a constant awareness of how much the opening of doors and the offering of glimpses during the early years depends on what is taught in school and learned only there.

From modern languages? Then you must deny the girl of 15, and therefore make very difficult for all young women, the power of direct personal communication in speech and writing with her equals and contemporaries in other countries in this close-knit, shrinking world. And you must stop the science faculties and the history schools of many universities from expecting (I nearly said demanding) that their students should come up to them with a competent reading knowledge of French and/or German.

From history, geography, divinity? Perhaps from somewhere here. But there are serious implications in any one of them, are there not?

Let us suppose that somehow we have acquired the time. Then we must find the teachers. Do we, in spite of all that has been said, fully grasp how many, and what sort? In a three-streamed girls' grammar school a modest increase of only five periods in science spread somewhere during the first three years will absorb half a teacher. To provide in every such school an additional 25 per cent of girls at the second stage, 14 to 16, with a 33 per cent science and mathematics curriculum content requires an additional quarter of a teacher. If in a school the sixth form totals 60 (it will in many schools be much more than that) and all the non-science specialists are to have a good science course as part of their sixth form education this will add over another quarter. These figures are very considerably below what would be required to implement for girls the suggestions contained in the pamphlet of the Science Masters' Association. Yet, modest as they are, they would require for every three grammar school streams throughout the country at least one whole highly qualified additional science specialist and, of course, a laboratory to work in. This leaves, remember, untouched the equally serious and important problem of other kinds of secondary schools or streams.

Nor is quantity all. There is only one fully guaranteed way, first to secure for all girls a thorough basic grounding in science, and then to ensure that a due proportion of them choose it as their specialism, and that the rest of them continue to pursue its study with pleasure and profit—and that is to sit them at the feet of an inspired teacher. The better the teacher the less does it matter, either to her or to her pupils, what amount of time she has. The duller the teacher the more disastrous to the popularity of the subject can be a generous time allowance and its consequent effects upon the choice of career. One inspired teacher of keen mind, rich personality and joyous skill, in love with her subject and in love with communicating it—only one such in a science department can revolutionize the attitude of a school and can sweep along with her those of lesser gifts till they too are moved above themselves.

Let there be no mistake about another point. We need the impact of this teacher not only in the sixth form but also in the main school, for reasons already sufficiently emphasized.

Quantity and quality are closely linked and both have for years now in girls' grammar schools been in serious and steady decline. Listen for a moment to the voices of actual head mistresses of specific schools speaking in their own words:

'I have advertised five times since October 1956 (for a senior mathematician) and have had one application from a young woman with no experience.'

That was the voice of the head mistress of a well-known boarding school.

'The chemistry (of this school) is being done by four part-time people, of whom only one is really satisfactory. Two are men, one of whom has taught for only one year—from 1914-15.'

'No applications for a chemistry post with an allowance of £275 attached to it. It is still vacant.'

28

That was the voice of a head mistress of a school in a great industrial area.

'A completely unqualified person on the staff who has taken her finals three times and failed, has now been awarded a pass General degree and has been given a permanent post here.'

'We have been without a chemistry and physics mistress for some years.'

That was the voice of a head mistress of a grammar school of 466 girls. And last, in reply to the question how many applicants for a science post, comes a crisp voice: 'None! I found him!'

In girls' schools there is, too, another growing handicap as compared with the situation in boys' schools—the increasing disappearance from the staff community of the women of 27 to 40 years of age. Early marriage and speedy promotion account for this. As the next decade comes and goes our girls' schools will be increasingly and ultimately almost completely, staffed by two kinds of women, the young professionally inexperienced woman in her first post learning her skills, and the older married woman returning, often part-time, after a gap of ten to fifteen years. There will, no doubt, be compensations and, in any case, successful adaptations to this situation, but I do not believe that we shall ever again return to anything like former standards of quantity and quality, and we must face it.

If you have a task to do with a limited labour force there is one way in which you can help yourself. What is needed is a time and motion study. In schools, that means a drastic overhaul of subject matter and method.

In course of time all subjects tend to get cluttered with the dead wood of old growth; vital new growth cannot flourish. In science it is time that a serious and concerted effort was made in two directions: First, a ruthless pruning of the factual content of school syllabuses in all the sciences at all the stages to let in the light and air of new thought and to give time and space for what the Science Masters admirably, though cautiously, call 'judicious digression to discuss matters of topical interest.' How one would like to change the word 'judicious' into 'reckless'—and the teacher of rare quality will do, of course, precisely that. Secondly, a drastic curtailment of some of the more tedious fatuities of certain kinds of practical work which still too often waste precious time and space in our laboratories,

29

and lamentably fail to command the respect of some of the abler pupils.

It needs no emphasis to realize that these reforms could take place tomorrow, given goodwill and determination by universities and examining bodies, and a strong lead from within the schools themselves.

These reforms would go a long way to redressing the balance of studies for the girls and therefore undoubtedly would help in increasing the number of girls going into scientific and technological careers, as well as reducing the number of women growing up with only a sketchy scientific knowledge to equip them for living their every-day lives in close company with scientific equipment amid great social and ethical problems posed afresh for humanity by modern science. Let it not be thought, however that an increase in the number of women entering science and technology depends only upon redressing the balance of their education. There are other important factors for girls to face which do not affect boys.

One of them is the difficult terms on which at present all along the line the girl has to compete with the boy. It is harder for her at 18 plus to secure a science place at a university, and not only because, having spent less time on scientific study she may score lower Advanced level marks than boys not intellectually her superiors, but also because in university department of physics, mathematics and chemistry, and in medical schools, there are many fewer places for women undergraduates than for men. Nor is getting in her only difficulty. If she gets a place in a science faculty and gets a good degree she still finds the scales weighted against her. Nearly every firm of repute will say, and sincerely mean in theory, that it will consider qualified women scientists and technologists. But, understandably, the greater long-term stability of a man in employment is an overwhelming factor in his favour. Man for woman he may be less good to begin with, but he is more likely to be able to give industry or a profession all his working life uninterruptedly. Once employed, the woman may not find it easy stage by stage to get to the top of her profession either, for, understandably, industry knows that at 25 or 26, however able she is, she is also unlikely to remain continuously in service much longer. But for her that very fact makes lack of promotion all the harder to bear.

The pattern of her own adult life places a handicap on the

woman scientist and technologist. For the great majority of women there is the certainty of a comparatively short period of initial employment, a very much longer period of absence from employment while they are raising their families and a return to a quite long period of employment after the family is launched. Every girl knows that she will certainly marry, and she will probably marry early—indeed, the situation is arising that she will have all she can do to complete her training between leaving school and getting married at 21 or 22. She will work till 26 or so and she will then work again from 40 to 60. This is not a bad prospect of life for a girl and it ought to encourage her to undertake worthwhile initial training whatever her career. But if the effect of two years' National Service has been an unsettling influence on boys, how much more is the prospect of a gap of ten or fifteen years to a girl? At 16 plus, at 18 plus one does not imagine oneself ever being 40 plus.

Even if a girl sets out to plan for that time with wholly unnatural foresight she might well ask herself certain questions in regard to science. During that 12 to 15 years' interval in which she will be very fully engaged with an altogether different kind of job the content of scientific knowledge will increase. New theories will develop. Techniques will change. She may find herself at 40 very much out of date. She may, too, be located in an area where her particular technology is not an easily marketable commodity. She will be very likely to have to re-enter her profession at a point where status and the prospects of promotion do not match her age and maturity. Is it, therefore, surprising that such a girl may play for safety and choose those careers where resumption at 40 plus after an interval seems to her less of a hazard and where chances of rising to positions of status and authority are still available; or, alternatively, where part-time employment is possible and where, so it may seem to her, though obviously she will have in any case a big adaption to make, some at least of her personal maturity and experience may be an actual asset to the job—teaching, nursing, medicine, dentistry, social work, the medical auxiliary professions, all may seem more attractive in this respect than careers in industry for the scientific girl.

With the exception of medicine they are, moreover, careers in which at every stage she can compete on even terms with boys and where in training she is less likely to be diverted or rejected. Even some of these have their difficulties. A young woman of 22 with a promising future as a trained nurse, writes that she is leaving the profession for training as an accounting machine operator at a bank. ' I am getting married this year. Nursing, if taken seriously and the work fulfilled, is a whole-time job. My fiancé goes to night school four nights a week for his B.Sc. degree. Obviously, one of us must not be so tired, and that one must be me.'

To the present inequalities of training and advancement, and to the later hazards of re-employment there are no easy answers. No doubt in the passage of time and in relation to the needs of the nation and of women themselves answers will be found. Even if, however, there were no answer, that would not be a reason to leave the present lop-sided state of girls' education unadjusted. We in education are not concerned only, not even mainly, with the vocational interests of our pupils or the economic needs of society. We are concerned with two other vital factors.

We must give our pupils the foundations of knowledge by which they may understand and take an intelligent part in the world in which they live. In that world science plays a part in every aspect of physical existence and of community living—in the home, in the field, in the factory, in peace and war, in sickness and in health, nationally, internationally and interplanetarily. Human judgment must be made about the effects of scientific processes, and such judgment is the responsibility of everyone, not merely of those expert in those processes. The surrender by the individual of his right to make judgments has already shown in our age the evil inherent in it. We have seen such surrenders caused by fear, by the worship of power. There is another kind of surrender of judgment—that due to ignorance. A girl must be given as much basic scientific knowledge as a boy, and not just because she is going to be the mother of children. The historic picture of domesticated women rocking the cradle with other children at her knee is a fading one. Father is again coming to bear a much more important—in fact an equal—part in the raising of his family, just as mother is coming to play a much more important—in fact an equal—part in life outside the home. Out of this will come a truer partnership, as yet imperfectly seen and fraught with difficult adjustments, but a state of affairs to which history has inexorably been moving and from which there is now no going back. It is therefore no more as mother than as father, no more as wife than as husband that young people must have scientific knowledge, and the girl must have it equally with the boy, as parent, worker, citizen, engaged equally with him in the intelligent running of home, industry, society.

There is still something more. When you have taught the girl enough science to give her the chance to choose a technological career and to enable her to share responsibility in the running of a scientific world you have not finished. The something more I am after is perhaps best suggested by the difference between the phrases ' standard of living ' and ' way of life.' We have come to see that science is not merely a means to speed, comfort, health, expanding our exports, getting rid of disease; but that it is in itself a thing of beauty, mysterious, wonderful, of exquisite order, truth and integrity, part of the road to heaven, and as such has a contribution to make to the intellectual and spiritual nurture of young people growing up, a contribution no less than that of literature, music and art. This is the supreme reason why we owe it to girls to redress the balance of their education.

DISCUSSION

Mr F. M. Brewer (*Reader in Inorganic Chemistry, University of Oxford*). I should like to take up what was almost the last question raised—that is the attitude of universities to examination syllabuses, and I include in that the attitude of examining boards. Nearly three years ago, at the Home Universities Conference, the Head Master of Winchester, the Head Mistress of the North London Collegiate School, and Professor Mott of Cambridge, discussed this particular point, and made an impassioned plea for a reduction in 'A' level syllabuses. I think that everybody at that Conference was probably in agreement with what was said. I got the Head Master of Winchester, Mr Lee, to start the ball rolling with the Oxford and Cambridge Board, of which he is a member, and that year that Board set about reducing all its syllabuses. There is really no difficulty about it, and I believe that all examining boards, if pressed by their school representatives adequately and persistently, will reduce their syllabuses too. They will be only too delighted to cut out the dead wood, because most of them do not want it there.

When the Oxford and Cambridge Board started they suggested, of course, cutting down the sciences first. I had experience of the committee which dealt with the chemistry syllabus, and it was the school masters not the University representatives who wanted to keep the old stuff in. They love teaching it; and although they can pay lip service to the fact that you ought to be teaching stuff which is not necessarily going to be examined, they all seemed scared of doing so.

I do hope that the Science Masters' Association will impress on their members the necessity for asking for this reduction, and that, incidentally, we shall have the same sort of reduction in history and English. We were told that we could not reduce the classics syllabus because there was not one. Incidentally, the biologists said they could not reduce theirs either. But it can, and ought to be, done, and it will be a great help to science in universities.

Although you may not believe me, I believe that every Oxford science tutor who looks at a candidate's papers is thoroughly suspicious of anything savouring of the last word on the subject. He would rather have the elements, and something to go with them outside the scientific interest. But the real thing we want to see is the maintaining of fresh interests, and the endeavour to get these things done in other fields and not only in science. I think that would help tremendously in making possible a general education which in the past, as my old tutor used to say to me, was ' an education in which science was left out.'

Dr KENNETH HUTTON (*Head Master, Hatfield School*). I am encouraged by the presence of my old tutor (Dr Brewer) and that of Sir Eric to act on the assumption that you should but ask and you shall receive. I am not going to talk particularly about science in schools or laboratories. What is particularly worrying me is the size of the classes in primary schools. The Ministry are alleged to be trying to bring about reductions. Yet, in point of fact, when the bulge is starting to come out of the primary schools, that is the moment when the Ministry are insisting on a reduction in the number of primary teachers. At least that is what is happening in Hatfield. We have had meetings of all the heads of schools in the town, and we find that primary school head masters are having teachers taken away from them. To my mind, that shows a shocking lack of planning by the Ministry three or four years ago—a failure to produce the teachers who inevitably were going to be required. I say now that we cannot possibly have properly educated scientists or non-scientists if the foundations are not properly laid in the primary schools.

I speak as a parent—I have four children. They have all been to the State primary schools, and within the limits that have been imposed upon the schools, they have been educated well. Two are still in primary schools, where the number of pupils in the classes is about 40. How can you teach really adequately if you do not plan successfully to produce more teachers to reduce the size of primary classes below 40? You certainly cannot get adequate teaching of mathematics. As I think will emerge later on in the discussion, unless we have proper teaching of mathematics in the early stages, the girls in particular become frightened of it; they go to training college and they ' skate over ' the mathematics there. They come out ill-qualified and so the teaching becomes worse and worse. Although I would not subscribe to the view that you cannot become an adequate scientist without a really good knowledge of mathematics, I would nevertheless say that even in teaching chemistry, which is less mathematical than physics, difficulties often arise because of the pupils' lack of mathematical knowledge. So I call upon the Ministry to do their duty and give back the teachers to the primary schools.

MR A. ARMSTRONG (*Physics Master, Sloane School, S.W.*). I should first of all like to correct Lord Heyworth on a couple of small points. He said that he questioned whether the scientist in industry was overpaid, or whether the science teacher was underpaid. Of course, the fact is that the scientist in industry is underpaid, and the science master is grossly underpaid.

He also referred to what Bernard Shaw had to say about the teaching profession. Mr Shaw said this in 1908; but in 1924 he said something quite different. Speaking of the efficiency of technical education, he said that the technical teacher knew his stuff and was anxious that his pupils should succeed. So obviously, when

35

he made the 'crack' about teachers, he was referring to the arts side.

Now I should like to make a small point with regard to Sir Solly Zuckerman's figures. He showed us that in a few years' time the number of people in the sixth forms will have greatly increased, due to the arrival of the bulge. He went on to say that the number of pupils going into universities and technical colleges will also have increased, but that the increase will not be fully comparable with the expansion of the sixth forms. In other words there will be a fall in the percentage of sixth form pupils who can go on to higher education.

I see a grave danger here. In spite of the very hopeful words of Dr Brewer, suggesting that we are going to have a reduction in our syllabuses, the standards demanded by the universities for entrants will become higher as competition for places becomes keener. I believe that is dangerous, because, though aiming at Scholarship standard is very nice and very interesting for the teacher, I do not believe it is good for all the pupils.

Making great and increasing intellectual demands upon our eighteen-year-olds has a drawback which is constantly being pointed out. This is, that by the time they are twenty or twenty-one, their minds are becoming so rigid, due to the weight of work put upon them, that fields of thought outside their specialism are entered only with the greatest difficulty. So these people who have been so heavily trained at seventeen or eighteen find difficulties later on. What is the value of the university demanding high standards if those high standards harm the minds of our best sixth formers?

MR L. H. SCOTT (*Head Master, City of Bath School*). May I refer to Sir Eric James's new law of the conservation of the curriculum. It has evolved pretty rapidly for one morning, because Miss Huxstep has suggested that part of the conservation could be achieved within the touch-lines and the goal-lines of the field of science itself.

We have already had the suggestion from the university end that if only the rigid-minded science teachers from the schools, who sit on examination bodies, were willing to give up teaching what they have taught for 20 or 30 years, and what they find easy and pleasant to teach, and were prepared to face the business of teaching something new, some progress could be made. The reason for that resistance should be made clear. The science teacher of 40 or 50 has been grossly overworked for 20 or 30 years, and if he is cautious about the new field which he is asked to enter, the reason is partly that overwork has made him rigid-minded and conservative. All the same I would like to endorse Miss Huxstep's view that we should try to reduce the science curriculum within the time at present allocated to science.

My own contribution to the development of Sir Eric James's important new suggestion is that we ought not at this time to accept the limits which he has, unconsciously I suppose, assumed —the limits of time which is available to us. Alexis Carrel was saying quite clearly 20 years ago in *Man, the Unknown*, that with the growth of human knowledge we must extend the period of education of our more able pupils. And what time could be more suitable for doing so in this country than the time when National Service is coming to an end? If we were given one year out of the two National Service years we could plan a three-year sixth form course in our schools. We cannot suggest adding a year to the university course because there will not be room in the foreseeable future. But it could be added to the school year and in many schools a start has been made. At an Institute of Physics Conference at Bristol a few years ago it was revealed that many university departments were basing their curricula on the assumption that their entrants had spent three years in the sixth form.

If you could make this change universal it would be possible to get round Sir Eric's difficulty, and combine general education with science specialism. Provided that science specialism is limited to its present degree or even slightly reduced, it would in fact be possible to do all the other things that we wish to do; but, as Sir Eric said in another place in January, the attempt to expand in this way brings us to one of the special problems of this Conference. We have not the laboratories in our schools, and we have not got the teachers to contemplate a universal third year. But I do hope that we shall follow up Sir Eric's proposals, and in doing so respect the great name of Alexis Carrel, and then we shall think in terms of a different rhythm and a longer and slower process of education, for our young people. In this way we may avoid the premature rigidity of so many over-crowded minds which find themselves unable at the universities to approach new knowledge with the freshness and zest and critical excitement with which new knowledge ought to be approached.

DR K. LAYBOURN (*Chief Inspector of Schools, Bristol*). I feel that some of us are thinking today that a different rhythm and a longer period of schooling in science is of vital necessity. Surely, then, with the prospect of the three years' course in the training colleges, we ought to be turning our minds to the problem of whether we are preparing our children in primary schools for the kind of science they ought to receive, and that we should want to teach them, in secondary schools.

This is my plea for the teaching of science in primary schools. It is a plea for an expansion of experience in those schools, such as will lead the children, when they become the young people in secondary schools, to begin to understand what the teacher is talking about, to begin to be interested in the subject, to want to learn more about it because they have had some personal experience of what the textbooks say is science.

I am greatly troubled at the way in which scientific laws and theories, in girls' schools particularly, are thrown at pupils who really have no hope whatever of ever experiencing what is being talked about. One of the things I have in mind is the way in which we teach plant cycles. With girls this subject is despatched in a very short time, and then they proceed to nutrition. These same girls may never have grown a plant from seed to seed. We speak of phases of light, continuing with shadows, and finishing up with a very specialized reference to eclipses to boys and girls who have never even observed the phases of the moon. We look at Sputniks; perhaps we ought to spend more time looking at what is always with us.

I would add my voice in support of the plea that has been made for smaller classes in primary schools, and also urge that the training colleges and universities should supply us with teachers for primary schools who can at least approach the realm of science. It is, of course, primarily a training college problem. These teachers should have some real experience, should have gone through the mill and learned something of what science means. I hope that we shall stop paying only lip service in primary schools by putting nature study on the curriculum for one period per week. We must do better than that.

MRS MERCER (*Lecturer in Physics and Bio-chemistry, Northern Polytechnic*). I am a lecturer in a domestic science department where we deal with girls who come from a variety of schools. They may come from secondary modern schools at the age of 16, or from secondary technical schools. They may be girls who have gone through the grammar school and have come on to us to study for institutional management examinations. Then, further, we have students who have taken institutional management or a nursing training, and are now working for a diploma in dietetics.

We require students who have a basic knowledge of the general principles of chemistry, physics and biology. I myself deal with the dietetic students, and I can speak especially of their needs. But I also have knowledge of the work that is being done with the students of institutional management, and I have a little knowledge of those who are doing City and Guilds cookery certificates, the demonstrators' certificates and housecraft certificates.

Those first-year students have to do a fair amount of science as applied to cookery and to housecraft. They require, therefore, a broad general knowledge of physics, chemistry and biology to understand what is happening in their technical work. For instance, in cookery they need to know enough chemistry to understand the functions of a raising agent; in laundry they need to know sufficient to understand what is happening when they use detergents; and to understand the demonstrators' course they need to know something about man-made textiles.

These things become clear to the students only if they can understand the principles which underly them. Some girls when asked what science they have done at school, merely laugh as though it were a great shock to them to be expected to know any science at all. Those are first-year students doing cookery and housecraft for the institutional management certificate. It is laid down that they should have five subjects at ' O ' level. I do not think that, until recently, science was compulsory. I am not quite certain that it is compulsory now, but we have asked for it to be so. On occasion girls come and they say that they could not do science at school because there was nobody who could teach it.

At one time I was faced with a class of first and second-year students—this is a three-year course—with one girl who had reached Advanced level, and another who had done no science whatever; and with a class composed in that way I was to give a series of lectures which included hygiene, physiology and the rudiments of chemistry. It is absolutely frustrating to have a class like that.

About the dietetics students I can speak more fully, because there we do insist that they have chemistry at Ordinary level. But I have found, from my own point of view, that it is far better if the students have taken a general science, including Paper III (Additional General Science) which I specially commend for girls who are going on to non-professional subjects. I have found it most useful, and it is my experience that a girl with that third paper has found her studies far less irksome than if she had only chemistry at Ordinary level. Of course students of dietetics besides following their ordinary curriculum should take other courses so that they have a comprehensive view of what will be required of them when they go into hospitals.

MR E. J. MACHIN (*Inspector of Schools, City of Birmingham*). Dr Laybourn has advocated the introduction of children to science at an earlier age. It may perhaps interest him to know that we have formed the same opinion in Birmingham. I had the privilege at Easter of opening a week's conference of teachers from the City primary schools when we studied the teaching of science in the primary schools, and we hope to present a report on it. We have carried out three separate experiments in the last year which have been most encouraging, the most important conclusion being that real interest, which responds readily to stimulus, seems to appear about the age of 9.

I am also interested in the suggestion from the Head Master of the City of Bath School about a longer period in the sixth form. Before I half escaped from teaching, some ten years ago, I was involved in such an experiment where, before the full implementation of the 1944 Act we normally got our sixth forms after a four year course which had ended with the old School Certificate. This was followed by a two-year course leading to Higher School Certificate. With the co-operation of my Head Master, I was able to have a three-year course in which we were able to devote each year rather less time to the main subjects and so to broaden our curriculum. There were benefits all round; the examination results were satisfactory and nearly all the people who entered that sixth form became professional scientists in one field or another.

A point that is new in this discussion—but I do not think that we should neglect it—is the potential supply of scientists and technologists or applied scientists, which is coming from those secondary modern schools which are able to give facilities for study beyond the age of 15. We are fortunate in that 25 per cent of such schools in Birmingham are giving such facilities, and without going into detail I can say that the results are extremely encouraging.

Mr L. Connell (*Lecturer in Education, Leeds University*). Much criticism has been levelled at examination syllabuses. I think myself that the 'O' level syllabuses are more or less right, but that they are often misinterpreted, particularly if emphasis is put in the wrong places. An example occurs to me of a boy who has been learning physics for six weeks. In the first three weeks, he ascertained the mass of a piece of brass. In the second three weeks, he ascertained its volume. By now I expect he has started on the next project and is dividing one by the other. Although density is a legitimate topic in an Ordinary level syllabus in physics, it is not as important as all that. But too many teachers seem to think it is.

My second point has to do with the award of open scholarships to the universities. An example of the figures shows that something like 20 per cent of open awards at Cambridge are in classics, whereas only 5 per cent of all G.C.E. 'A' level entries are in classics; but more than 40 per cent of 'A' level entries are in science, while only 22 per cent of the Cambridge awards are in science. I may be told that it will be difficult to change the system of open awards so that they bear some relation to the number of sixth-formers taking the different subjects, but I think that that difficulty should be overcome, because it has a serious effect on schools. It gives some schools a reason for encouraging the best people not to do science, or for letting them drop it as early as possible even in the third or fourth form. What the best people do, many of the second-best people want to follow.

My third point concerns the Latin requirement for entry to some universities. Miss Huxstep, this morning, was trying to find time for science for the girls and was reluctant to take it from Latin. I feel sure that if the teaching of Latin were freed from the university examination requirement, so that for the first time it was taught only to the children who wanted to learn it for some better reason, Latin would begin to be taught better than it has been in the past. If the compulsion were removed and the time devoted to Latin were reduced, more science could be taught. Nothing encourages correct teaching as much as the knowledge that if you do not teach well, you will have no class to study your subject.

Miss A. M. Almond (*Head of Science Department, County Girls' Grammar School, Newbury*). I would like to follow Miss Huxstep's address this morning by a practical suggestion which might help in a small way to increase the number of scientists coming from girls' schools. We cannot produce more scientists unless we have more science teachers.

The British Federation of University Women has recently been trying to encourage various authorities to hold refresher courses for women who have been out of teaching, or have never been in it, and are now available to go into teaching later in life, either full-time or part-time. A pilot course has just been held at Reading, directed by Sir Graham Savage. About 25 women came out of seclusion and studied physics and chemistry for a fortnight, and were extremely stimulated thereby. Even if only some of those are able to help in our girls' schools, they will make a valuable contribution.

What you in this audience can do to help is to encourage the people in your districts to do likewise. First of all comb out those who are thinking they are too rusty to go back to teaching; then having created a demand approach the local authorities and institutes of education for the establishment of courses.

Mr E. W. Hawkins (*Head Master, Calday Grange Grammar School, West Kirby, Cheshire*). I wish to make two points very tentatively. The first one may show slight disagreement with Sir Eric James about arts boys in the sixth forms taking 'A' level science. If I understood Sir Eric correctly, he thinks that if we have historians doing examination physics, they will be doing it unwillingly and they will not get much out of it because their hearts will really be in their history.

I wonder whether we are, perhaps, thinking, Sir Eric James and I, about different sorts of sixth-former and whether, in some of our discussions on the sixth-form syllabus, we do not have in mind two different kinds of sixth form. I think there is an essential difference between a sixth form which has a high degree of selection and which has the privilege of seeing Sir Eric James every day, and the sixth form which has the very different privilege of seeing me. They are not the same kind of community.

If I were to propound a law for my own sixth form—I doubt whether Sir Eric would accept it—it would be like this: the dimmer they are, the more they need a broad sixth-form course and the less they like it.

The sixth-formers who are right at the top of the tree will take the kind of broad science course that Sir Eric James spoke about, that inspiring course that he outlined to us, but I would say that the dimmer ones at the bottom require the stimulus of taking something as an 'A' level subject. It has been suggested that we might have four 'A' subjects as a minimum, two of them being, say, physics and maths and two of them history and German. That would seem to me to be a properly balanced course. It would entail, of course, some pruning of content in each subject, but I think there are advantages for the maintained grammar schools in having more subjects examined at 'A' level.

My other point is a much more solid one. I wonder how much damage is done in the introduction of mathematics to our younger children—I speak as the father of one aged 10 who is facing the 11-plus examination—by the quite fantastic rigmarole of parlour tricks which they have to learn with our British weights, measures and currency. Are we not frightening children away from mathematics by making it appear that they have to give the best years of their lives—that is, between 9 and 11, when their chief interest is in going to the pond to catch newts and in exploration and adventure —to learning conversions of bushels, quarters, gallons, pints, farthings and pounds.

One useful contribution that this Conference might make is to send out a very clear call that we will no longer tolerate the wrong view of mathematics which is given to young children, and all the

43

loss of our national time which is entailed by our antiquated system of weights and measures and currency; and that the sooner we get that dead wood cleared out of the curriculum, the better.

MR C. A. RONAN (*Staff, Royal Society*). I have done a little work for the University of London Extra-mural Department and one or two points have arisen from it which might possibly be of interest, especially in view of some of the remarks of Sir Eric James. He said this morning, if I heard him correctly, that there was no gulf between the disciplines of the humanities and the sciences in their modes of thought; both are rationalized systems. Surely, however, the great factor that science in the schools must take into account is that scientific activity in these days is characterized by an experimental approach. This conception was probably one of the foundation stones of the Royal Society.

I believe that in some schools, different from those of my day, boys and girls are now taught something of the experimental approach, but from what I hear I suspect that the experiments they do in the laboratory are not experiments in the true sense but are, as it were, time spent in practical self-demonstration. Surely, it is vital that both those who are going forward in science, and those who are going to do other things but who nevertheless should have some science teaching, should have this experimental approach brought home to them. They should be given a problem to solve, the result of which they do not know. They can be led so far and should go on from there.

I am led to that conclusion because at a couple of summer schools during the last two years, a small course was carried out for the University of London in which certain scientific principles were discussed with non-scientists. They were set an experimental problem, the answer to which they did not know, and they all got reasonable results. One of the things that came out, however, was that they said they now understood why so many persons who worked in scientific research gave their results in a very carefully qualified way: e.g., ' It would seem that under certain conditions, such and such happens.' This was something they had not realized before. They were delving into the unknown; therefore, they could not be exactly certain of their results—at least, not on one experiment. About one experiment was all that there was time for at these schools.

I should like to mention two other points. I agree that it seems difficult to bring science to those who are not primarily interested in it, by teaching the history or the philosophy of science. Surely, however, one of the problems is to show the development of scientific thought. I do not think personally that this is quite so difficult as it seems at first.

If you take an old shove-ha'penny board, push a halfpenny across it and ask schoolboys why it stops, most of them will reply: 'Ah, friction.' That is fair enough, but there were other explanations in past times which served equally well. The reason why we now adopt the conception of friction is, I suggest, primarily due to the fact that in accepting it we accept a whole new outlook, which began with Newton and which is far more widely embracing of the world around us than was the outlook of Aristotle.

Surely, then, there is a lesson to be learnt and something that can be brought home to the non-scientific pupil: namely, that one of the things that the scientist does in his research and in the theories he brings from it, is to give a wider and a more embracing picture of the universe. This should give some idea of the excitement and the thrill of scientific work. This is surely something which science teachers—who are qualified to think about it— should spend some time in considering.

Is there not also another great problem, not only with science pupils, but also with those who are specializing in other work, in giving explanations of current scientific ideas which cannot always be fitted into a nice, pretty, every-day picture?

We all know the Festival of Britain picture of the atom, with the nucleus in the centre and the electrons going around. I wonder how many schoolchildren who saw it thought that it was just an atom writ large, just a great, magnified picture. Surely, it is a symbol picture which is convenient for our minds to use. Possibly this is an extremely erudite thing to try to get over, but I am sure that there are forms of explanation which children could understand in order to realize that some of the things that they will read in books and learn about, are not, in fact, actual magnified models of the universe as it is understood, but symbol pictures. In other words, a note on the music stave has as much relationship to the sound it stands for as the Festival of Britain picture of an atom has to the atom itself. It seems to me that if these things are thought about, we might make it easier for the science teacher to expound scientific concepts for those who are not at first interested in them or aware of them.

MRS A. YOUNG (*Silverthorne Secondary School, London, S.E.*1). I have listened carefully to this morning's discussion and to the addresses, but I have not heard much mention of the secondary modern school. I am fully aware that we need facilities for the élite of the population, but we must not forget that 80 per cent are in secondary modern schools. Very often these boys and girls may seem dim—as somebody said—when they are at school, but when they leave school and go into work a number of them make great progress in evening classes, and some become members of professional engineering associations.

It is very difficult to teach in a secondary modern school; but these schools will produce most of the technicians and they are therefore entitled to a share of the best brains. We have to cope with much greater difficulties than the grammar schools. One laboratory has to serve for everything. We have one period a week allowed for science. Sometimes it is only 45 minutes, or sometimes it is a double period. That period has to cover everything, and very often it is only put on the syllabus to appease the powers that be, who are often more interested in the teaching of shorthand and typewriting.

I plead for a much better attitude to the modern schools, particularly on the part of some of the grammar school teachers, who seem to think that all who come to the modern schools are failures and that nothing can be done for them. I wonder what would have happened to the late Professor Einstein, who, I believe, was not good at examinations when he was young, or to Michael Faraday, had they been living now. I therefore urge that when we reach our conclusions they will include something for the secondary modern school, because it is most rewarding to teach in one of these schools.

SIR SOLLY ZUCKERMAN. I am glad that it is Sir Eric who will have the last word. I intervene only because of what struck me as an extremely important point made by Mr Armstrong in this morning's discussion when he referred to the danger that rising standards of admission to higher education would intensify specialization when we all wish to postpone it. Looking at the whole problem from the outside, I can see how serious is his dilemma.

On the one hand, we have had the discussion about the content of sixth-form education, which Sir Eric raised, and the hope that it may be broadened and liberalized. On the other hand, the future looms ahead with prospects of greater competition. I do not want to lay too much stress on the figures in detail, but they do seem to point to the conclusion that ten years hence probably not more than about 50 per cent of the sixth forms will be able to get into the stream of higher education, using that term in the broadest possible way.

My conclusion is that the quality of those individuals who will be selected for the higher education will inevitably rise. And the problem of deciding what the content of the sixth-form education should be—how you generalize education, how you produce specialization, how you make the task of a university selector easier—will become more difficult than it is today. It is well to be clear about what is likely to happen on the trend of the figures and to prepare for it in advance.

SIR ERIC JAMES. I cannot let Mr Hawkins get away with that curriculum. He suggested that for the dim sixth-former, the not very clever boy, a course consisting of history, German, mathematics and physics all at 'A' level, would be good. I think there is a chance that such a curriculum might receive approval. It is important, therefore, that we should stamp on it now.

Here is a person who is not terribly clever by definition, not a real ' fizzer.' He is doing mathematics and physics to the 'A' level. I forgot whether Mr Hawkins is a scientist, but I assure him that mathematics at 'A' level is particularly difficult. Now think of the amount of reading that history to 'A' level should involve, if it is to be anything except a repetition of notes. If, then, you add a language, so that the man must have a linguistic ability, even when he is *ex hypothesi* dim, you will see that his life will be a fairly full one.

What will he have got at the end of it? He will have learned

47

enough physics—physics only—to get through at 'A' level. He will be able to solve a certain number of differential equations, as I did when I took 'A' level mathematics, without really understanding them. That will be his grasp of science. Is this the preparation which will enable him in future to converse with chemists, biologists, biochemists and medical research workers. Is it? No, it is not.

What is worse—this is why I feel passionately about it—is that the great fault in our general education is not that we are making too great intellectual demands, as somebody said. On our cleverest boys, the actual intellectual demands are not too great. What is really wrong is that we are over-filling their lives. Above all, we are not giving them time to read.

This boy of Mr Hawkins, doing history, German, mathematics and physics to 'A' level certainly could not, especially if he is also a Scout, and is playing football for the second XI, and trying to get a Trevelyan scholarship. That boy obviously will never read a single book between the ages of 16 and 18. That is abundantly clear. If once we could get these people reading, we could stop talking about general education and go quietly home!

My last point concerns the gulf between science and arts. I know that there is a thing called the experimental method and I suppose that it represents something peculiar to science. Does it, I wonder? How many pictorial artists have indulged in the experimental method? When one looks at all those canvases and all those sketches one is surely reminded of the experimental method at work. And is not the same true of other fields?

I think it is a pity if we say that there are scientists and that they move in a mysterious way their wonders to perform, and that they have this curious technique that marks them off from the arts person. In actual fact, anyone who has ever done scientific research even in a very humble way knows perfectly well that what really makes one tick is the tremendous desire for order or system, or whatever one likes to call it.

This scientists' technique perhaps makes more use of controlled experiment than is made by those who work in arts and letters, but nevertheless we shall magnify our difficulties if we accentuate the gulf between the scientist on the one hand, and the arts man on the other. That is why, on the whole, I deplore this idea of the unrelated subject.

SESSION II

SCIENCE TEACHING—THE PRESENT POSITION

Mr. F. L. Allan, Chairman

In introducing this session, I should like, as a school master, to speak for myself and, I am sure, for other school masters in saying how immensely we value and appreciate what has been done by the British Association in this matter, for their imaginative vision and their energy and their sense of public duty in arranging this Conference.

They have been true to their name in a more literal sense too. They have done something very British. This occasion is essentially British—or, perhaps it would be truer to say, essentially English. We are met together to examine a situation which is critical for the national future, and yet this is essentially a private conference. The British Association itself takes pride in the fact that it is an independent body. Those who speak either from the platform or from the floor speak in the capacity of private persons. The whole thing is very much in the English idiom. When Napoleon said, if he did say it, that the English were a nation of shopkeepers, I fancy that in a moment of irritation he was regarding this more civilized nation as being out of step with him. He, therefore, accused them of being amateurs, at any rate in the field in which he himself was a professional and the expert.

The contention that the English are a nation of amateurs can, however, be readily sustained. I think that we are a nation of amateurs, both for good and for ill, very often exasperatingly amateur; and at this moment, perhaps, our country is just becoming aware of its difficult situation. It is in this very situation that this meeting has been arranged.

It is almost as if this Conference and the atmosphere in which we meet were part of a repetitive process, or a stage in a kind of cyclical movement in English history. The Association itself was founded in 1831 to convince an indifferent public and Government

49

that science was important and worth backing. That situation in 1831 was, in essence, the very one we are facing at this moment.

We can take comfort from the fact that a nation of amateurs has all the great amateur virtues too. Although it takes this country a matter of years to realize that there is a critical situation, once the point has been seized there is no nation on earth which takes itself by the scruff of the neck so thoroughly and vigorously, and organizes itself into possibly the most formidable power that history has seen. One hopes that the same result will emerge from the present crisis.

We are speaking about a particular section of education, and in the background, of course, is the fact, which is recognized by all speakers, that science is only a component of a full education, as Sir Eric James demonstrated so well this morning. We are not arguing, and probably shall not begin to argue, that science is opposed to any other of the intellectual or humanistic disciplines.

What we are concerned with now is not the grand design of education, the grand strategy or even the tactics. We are dealing rather with what the Americans would call the ' logistics,' and those who are going to speak to you will use not so much the language of Churchill as that of Alanbrooke. We are going to hear in what way we are deficient in the two essential elements, namely teaching staff and equipment.

That really is the heart of our whole enterprise. We wish to bring home our convictions to the country as a whole, and to those who make decisions on national policy.

Sir Winston Churchill has said, ' If you have a good point, it is not enough merely to state it once or twice. You must go on stating it and hammer it home.' We hope that one effect of this Conference will be that the public at large and the more intelligent of the responsible parties who are chiefly concerned with providing for education will take note of the two main problems on which we are to be illuminated this afternoon.

THE SUPPLY OF SCIENCE TEACHERS

Dr A. W. Barton

Since 1939, there has been a social revolution trying to make England into one country again. The 1944 Education Act carried the revolution into the schools by laying down that all children shall be educated in accordance with their age, ability and aptitude. This ideal is being realized for secondary education by supplementing the pre-war secondary grammar school, which catered for the child of some academic ability, with the new secondary modern school, which is to provide a general education for the average child of 11-16 years of age. It took the grammar school fifty years to establish itself. It will take the modern school as long, and perhaps even longer, because, unlike the grammar school, the modern school has no pattern on which to model itself.

It will be seen, therefore, that the three partners who run the national system of education—the Ministry of Education, the local education authorities and the teachers—have got their hands full. As if that was not enough, the natural forces which we cannot control have produced an unusually high birthrate in the 1940's which is now finding its way through the schools. It is raising the secondary school population from 2 million in 1950 to 2,900,000 in 1961, so that the three partners in our national system of education have recently had to provide 30,000 extra teachers to cope with that birthrate bulge.

It is not really true to say, as Mr Hutton did this morning, when he was complaining about the primary schools being deprived of their teachers, that the Ministry of Education have not planned. They have planned a great deal in the last ten years, and the fruit of that planning is the arrival of 30,000 extra teachers in the last five years to ensure that the classes in primary and secondary schools, which we all agree are still too big, did not get completely out of hand. We should pay a tribute to the three partners for the work they have done on this plan.

Although there are still not enough ordinary teachers, there is also a shortage of specialist teachers for the secondary modern schools in such subjects as housecraft, handicrafts, physical education, music and scripture. If you are to provide a secondary education for each child in accordance with his age, ability and aptitude, you must offer in the secondary modern schools good courses of a secondary character leading in these subjects to something comparable with 'O' level in the academic subjects. You cannot do that without specialist teachers. At present not only are there insufficient specialist teachers but too many of them are not properly qualified.

None of these shortages, however, is so important to the future of the nation as the need for more scientists and technologists about which we heard this morning from Sir Solly Zuckerman. The 4 per cent increase in national output demands the doubling about every ten years of the annual output of science graduates, whose training begins in the sixth forms of our schools. Nothing, therefore, is so important to the future of the nation as the science that is taught in the grammar schools and in the public schools and in those secondary modern schools that are providing G.C.E. courses. (Like Miss Huxstep, I am using the word science to include mathematics).

Therefore, the grammar schools are important, because they must be well supplied with science teachers if the annual output of science graduates is to be increased.

I shall now try to give you the facts about the supply and quality of science teachers in the public and grammar schools before the war, in 1953, and today. I shall state what steps have been taken to improve the supply and quality and suggest what steps could be taken and should already have been taken to produce some real improvement in the situation. I shall conclude by venturing to suggest two proposed courses of action which, I hope, will emerge from this Conference. This follows Sir Ben Lockspeiser's lead this morning, when he exhorted the Conference not only to discuss but to act.

In 1938, all posts in maintained grammar schools for boys were filled. In that year, 60 per cent of the students entering those schools as teachers from the university departments of education held first or second class honours degrees, and 15 per cent of them had firsts. It was a rare occurrence to find in a public school a teacher with a third or a pass degree. There were practically no non-graduates teaching science in public and grammar schools. In fact there were some science graduates who could not get science posts and were teaching subjects like woodwork and physical education. The situation was much the same in the girls' schools.

In 1953, over 100 science posts were unfilled in the maintained grammar schools for boys, and only 39 per cent of the men entering those schools from the university departments of education in that year had first or second class honours degrees and only 4 per cent had firsts. The public schools were having to appoint an increasing number of men with indifferent degrees whom they would not have considered before the war, and the girls' schools were suffering similar difficulties.

In 1957, in the maintained grammar schools for boys and girls, there were still 103 posts unfilled and there was no prospect of filling 148 new posts needed to deal with larger sixth forms; 222 posts were unsatisfactorily filled and 614 posts were held by non-graduates. Before the war, therefore, the posts in these schools were almost all filled with graduates of whom about 60 per cent had first or second class honours degrees. In 1957, in round figures, 1,100 posts out of a total of 7,000—about one-seventh of them—in maintained grammar schools were either unfilled or unsatisfactorily filled. That is a deplorable decline from the good staffing of these schools before the war and a decline which is contrary to the spirit and the intention of the 1944 Education Act.

This statistical survey of the situation is confirmed and made more realistic by a glance at the situation in one or two individual schools. In 1923, an ordinary public school with no particular reputation in science teaching had a science staff of five, two firsts and three seconds. A third physics post was created in 1925, and for the next 14 years the school was always able to get a man with a second, and twice it got a man with a first, to fill it. In 1938, the school had a science staff of seven, two Ph.D.s, three firsts and two seconds, and it recruited all its new men straight from the university.

On the other hand, since the war, a distinguished public school with some reputation for science teaching has only been able to recruit scientists with good honours degrees by taking them away from other schools; when it has recruited straight from the university, it has had to appoint men with third class or pass degrees, men whom it would not have considered before the war—except for two, recently appointed, who were deferred from National Service.

In the last few years, no school that I have heard of has interviewed candidates for science vacancies. The candidates make a tour of half a dozen schools; they interview the schools and they finally decide where they want to go. I know of one young man who has not yet got his degree at Oxford, who recently went to five good schools in a week. I venture to state that none of them would have looked at a man with his qualifications before the war. Now he has virtually chosen his school.

We have heard that the annual output of scientists and technologists in this country is to be doubled again in the next few years. It was 5,000 in 1945 and 10,000 in 1955 and it should be 19,700—or, in round figures, 20,000—by 1970. The grammar schools played their full part in the doubling between 1945 and 1955 by increasing the size of their sixth forms, which are today two or three times their pre-war size and which may increase still more. The size of the science sixths in the public and grammar schools—boys' and girls'—is today about 31,000. We think we may bring them up to 39,500.

I was interested to listen to Sir Solly Zuckerman's account of the automatic way in which the size of sixths and the science departments of universities was going to increase. My figures, which refer to science sixths only, confirm this, and my increase of 8,500 includes an extra 2,500 in the girls' schools; it is based upon an estimate which assumes that at the end of this period about 60 per cent of all the boys *and girls* in the sixth forms will be specializing in science. That is, I think, the maximum that we can afford to have if we are to maintain the aesthetic and spiritual quality of our national life and are not to become the slaves of the scientific machines that we are inventing.

The girls' schools are shorter of science teachers than the boys' schools, and particularly of teachers of physics and chemistry in the sixth forms. If the schools are to teach an extra 8,500 boys and girls in the science sixths, they must have 700 more graduate science teachers than they have at the moment. How are they to get them when 1,100 posts are still either vacant or unsatisfactorily filled? Furthermore, an increase in the science sixths of the above order of magnitude, coming on top of the growth since 1939, can be achieved only if we have first-class teachers capable of attracting a greater proportion of boys and girls to specialize in science. The pupils tend to follow the best teachers rather than the subject and they do not really know much about the urgent need for scientists and technologists.

An increase of 8,500 in the size of grammar school science sixths means that about 4,000 more science specialists will leave these schools each year, and I am assuming that all of those will be good enough to get into a university to read for a science degree. So we have still to find each year another 5,000 or 6,000 boys and girls if we want to double the present annual output of 10,000 who can obtain a graduate qualification in science. They will presumably come from the bilateral schools or the secondary modern schools providing G.C.E. courses. I was glad to hear a mistress from one of those schools talking about the difficulties of their work to which I am glad to draw attention. In 1957, there were 877 secondary modern schools providing 'O' level courses. They had 89 unfilled posts, 152 new posts to be filled, 177 unsatisfactorily filled and 1,375 non-graduates teaching science. They probably need an additional 300 science teachers if they are to increase by 5,000 the annual output of those who are qualified to enter apprenticeships leading ultimately to associate membership of engineering institutions. For all types of school, therefore, we must find somewhere about 1,000 more science teachers, if we are to supply the necessary number of children qualified to enter graduate courses at the universities and technical colleges to enable the annual output of scientists and technologists to be increased from 10,300 in 1955 to 19,700 in 1970.

Before the war, the grammar schools were well staffed, largely with teachers with good honours degrees. Why are they short of science staff now? There are, I think, four reasons. The schools need more teachers for their sixth forms, which are now two or three times as big as they were before the war. Universities have about doubled the size of their science staffs between 1945 and 1955. Industry and the Government are using far more science graduates than they did before the war. The truth is, of course, that at the moment there are not enough scientists to go round.

The salary of science teachers before the war was comparable with that paid by the other professions open to them, such as the universities, the Scientific Civil Service and industry. Today, it is inferior, in spite of the recent increases in the Burnham Scales. Finally, before the war the maintained grammar schools were administered in the same sort of way as the public schools, and these maintained schools and their staffs were beginning to enjoy the same sort of prestige as the public schools. The 1944 Education Act naturally introduced one code of administration for all schools. Some local education authorities have decided to administer the new secondary modern schools as they used to, and still do, administer the grammar schools, but many local education authorities now administer all their schools, including their grammar schools, as they used to administer the elementary schools. The result has been that the prestige of the maintained grammar schools has tended to decline and work in them is no longer as attractive as it used to be.

Four steps have been taken since the war to increase the supply and quality of grammar school science teachers. Their salaries have been improved. For example, in 1948, a senior science master got £800 a year. Today, he gets £1,400 a year. The age of retirement for teachers was raised in 1955 from 65 to 70, thus enabling science teachers to continue for five more years. Men with first or second-class honours degrees in science going to teach in grammar schools have been deferred from National Service since January, 1956. These last two measures, welcome as they are, will bring only a temporary relief. The first will end by 1960, and the second is already over in 1958.

Finally, neighbouring schools have been encouraged to share science teachers, particularly in sixth form work, but little has been achieved for various good reasons. In any case, this is a defeatist step in these days, for in the present situation schools with small science sixth forms should not be encouraged to share science teachers with others but to expand their classes until they are full.

What else can now be done to improve the supply and quality of science teachers? Three or four years ago the Ministry of Education published a pamphlet putting the claims of teaching as a career to university graduates. This should be supplemented by regular visits to the universities of distinguished directors of education, head masters and science masters to put the claims of teaching to third-year science undergraduates. Two or three such visits made at the invitation of universities have been quite successful, and I hope that discussion by the Committee of Vice-Chancellors and representative head masters next month will result in regular arrangements being set up for them.

The Ministry of Education should encourage local education authorities to introduce a trial period of teaching in schools for undergraduates during their long vacations, analogous to the works courses arranged by industry to attract recruits. When I look at the drive, initiative and imagination shown by industry in these days of full employment to attract recruits for the important work that it has to offer, I am bound to express my disappointment at the efforts made by the Ministry of Education to attract recruits for grammar school teaching. We have nothing to be ashamed of. We have a fine job to offer these young men, but in times like these we have to go out to tell them about it. Let them see for themselves what sort of persons we are, how keen we are on our job after doing it for thirty years, and then they will be able to decide if teaching is a satisfying and important job.

A good science teacher has to be equally interested in persons and in his subject. Unlike the humanities, science does not make its students necessarily interested in other people. In pre-war days when there was unemployment, some people were forced by the economic situation to take up teaching whether they liked it or not. That is not likely to happen any more. Therefore, it is essential that the universities should set out deliberately to produce people who will be interested both in persons and in things, by arranging honours degree courses including both arts and science subjects, and by doing their best to encourage undergraduates who look as if they have the right sort of qualities for teaching to take up such courses.

It is a fact that scientists at present are in short supply. Sir Solly Zuckerman this morning said that a census of the present science graduates and engineering graduates has been taken for the Advisory Council on Scientific Manpower. So they apparently know the distribution of scientists among the various bodies using them. I feel, however, that the Government should arrange a conference of these bodies who employ science graduates—the universities, industry, Government departments and the schools—who could have before them the material that Sir Solly Zuckerman's Committee already have, so that they can know the distribution of available scientists between these parties. An interdepartmental committee should then be set up with authority to ensure that the distribution of the available science graduates between those who employ them is in the best interests of the country. That is what we did when we were short of food during the war. We must do the same sort of thing now that we are short of expert scientists. This does not imply the direction of labour. It can be done by control of vacancies or establishments.

The National Advisory Council on the Supply and Training of Teachers published a report in 1953 on the supply of mathematics and science graduates for the secondary schools. In that report, the Council said that the shortage of science teachers would have serious long-term effects both on the education of the nation and on the future supply of scientists and technologists, and they implied the need for co-operation between the various bodies using scientists. I wonder why they did not try to take the initiative in arranging a conference of the sort that I have suggested. The Federation of British Industries expressed the same view and arranged a conference in January, 1954; and now, the British Association is helping to get it expressed again.

Immediate steps should therefore be taken to ensure that the distribution of available scientists among the bodies who use them is made in the best interests of the nation. We have had this problem ever since the war. We have talked about it long enough. It is time that something was done.

Although there has been a big increase in the salary of all teachers since 1950, the good science teacher is still underpaid and the grammar schools will go short of science teachers until this is put right. In 1938, a university lecturer rose to £500 per annum, a graduate master in an elementary school rose to £384 and a graduate in a grammar school to £480 per annum. A senior lecturer or a reader at a university rose to £600 a year, and a senior science master rose to £576.

The corresponding figures today are as follows: the university lecturer rises to £1,650 and a grammar school science master to £1,075, a university reader to £2,100 and a senior science master to £1,400. Perhaps the grammar school masters were overpaid in 1938. But they are now certainly underpaid.

If we are to achieve a 4 per cent annual increase in

production the grammar schools must play their part. They will not get the men and women to do so unless their salaries are improved.

One other factor which influences the careers chosen by undergraduates is what their professors and lecturers do. For the last 40 years the university science faculties have over-emphasized the importance of research and have tended to neglect the importance of teaching. Let me give a specific example. Before Lord Rutherford came to be Professor of Physics at Cambridge in 1919, it was laid down in the statutes that the professor should give a course of lectures to first-year students on the properties of matter and on electricity and magnetism. After the first year, he got that statute abolished, and that course of lectures is no longer given by the professor. In my opinion, when that statute was abolished one of the seeds of the shortage of science teachers was sown. It led to the belief that the one thing that really mattered in universities was research.

At the North of England Education Conference two and a half years ago, the Vice-Chancellor of Sheffield University said that we appoint our lecturers because of their ability in research and the teaching seems to get done somehow. I wonder whether it does get done. If you ask some of the undergraduates, they would express a quite different opinion.

It is because professors and lecturers are so obviously enthusiastic about research and indifferent about teaching that so few of the science graduates of the universities are taking up teaching. Only when the universities again take their teaching seriously will a reasonable proportion of their undergraduates feel that teaching in a school is a worthwhile and honourable career.

To sum up, before the war the grammar schools were fully staffed with science graduates of a good quality. For the last ten years, they have been unable to fill many of their vacancies and the quality of their science staffs has deteriorated. The 1957 survey quoted earlier, supports this view. The steps so far taken to improve the situation—increases in salary, later retirement and the deferment of National Service—have only prevented the situation from getting worse. Today, about one-seventh of the science posts in grammar schools are either unfilled or unsatisfactorily filled and there appears to be no hope of getting the 1,000 extra teachers who are needed to prepare for the second doubling of the annual output of scientists and technologists.

It was never the intention of the 1944 Education Act that the standard of the grammar school should deteriorate. It is therefore unjust that the present situation should continue. It is also unwise in view of the fact that the economic output of the country cannot increase without the doubling to which I have just referred.

The country has now reached the moment of decision. If it wants to maintain and improve its material and cultural standard of life in the modern competitive technological world, it must have more scientists and technologists. This in turn means more and better science teachers first in the grammar schools and then in the secondary modern schools.

The country has now to decide whether it is willing to recognize the value of the specialist to the country, whether he is a teacher, a doctor or a man who works with his hands, a craftsman. The country must now take the necessary steps to see that these specialists are encouraged and suitably rewarded; but in particular it must see that the schools are properly supplied with graduate science teachers of good quality. That may even mean for a short time some slowing down of improvements in the staffing and building of secondary modern schools and primary schools, the need for which all of us here fully accept and will fully support; but if the country shirks the decision which I have mentioned, because of its unpopularity in some quarters, we shall fall behind, and we shall deserve to fall behind, the other countries of the world, and with that our hopes of improving the standard of life and of providing a real secondary education for all will slowly but surely fade away.

I hope, then, that this Conference will decide to do two things. The first is to ask the British Association to appoint a deputation, and to ask the Minister of Education to receive that deputation, so that they can impress upon him the importance of the recruitment of more and better science teachers for the grammar schools, for the technical schools and for those secondary modern schools which provide G.C.E. 'O' level courses. Secondly, I hope that the British Association will form a deputation and ask, say, the Lord President of the Council to receive it, in order that it can be represented to him that scientists are at the moment in short supply, and that there are no prospects of attaining an adequate supply in the foreseeable future. Therefore, he should set up an interdepartmental committee to find the facts about the present distribution of the available scientists among the interests who use them. Then appropriate steps should be taken to ensure that future distribution is in the best interests of the country.

ACCOMMODATION AND EQUIPMENT

Dr H. F. Boulind

Dr Barton has rightly spoken first in this session on the present position in science teaching, because he has dealt with the men and the women who are needed to do the teaching, while my task is to deal with the material equipment which they and their pupils use. Men are obviously more important than material—many teachers achieve excellent results with the most makeshift equipment—and all honour to them! No amount of apparatus and other facilities, however, can make up for the lack of an inspiring, intelligent and resourceful teacher. But, having said that, we must certainly put the necessary equipment as the second requirement. Without adequate laboratory facilities, the science teacher lives in an atmosphere of frustration: either his teaching tends to become entirely theoretical, or he spends, on various kinds of improvisation, time which he should devote to the improvement of his teaching. In other words, he becomes discouraged, he thinks wistfully of the facilities available in university and industrial laboratories, and his teaching becomes ineffective. It is uneconomic to employ a good worker and then refuse him the tools with which to do the job.

Perhaps I may be allowed to dwell for a few moments on those four words 'his teaching becomes ineffective.' Why is he teaching science? What are the primary aims of science teaching? Least of all subjects in the school curriculum, should science be on the teacher's part a matter of dogmatic exposition, and on the pupil's part a matter of routine memorization of laws and principles for subsequent regurgitation in one of the sillier and less imaginative types of public examination. Science education may have many aims and objects, but surely the main object can be stated in one word: it is to make pupils *think*, to lead them to formulate problems clearly, and to attempt to solve them in a common-sense, scientific manner. You cannot make pupils think solely, or even mainly, by talking at them, and you certainly cannot produce scientists that way. Any science course needs to be firmly rooted in practical work of the type that uses experiment as a means of solving problems, and in which stress is laid upon the importance of correct techniques. How can interest in science, the overwhelming interest that all pupils have when they first enter our grammar school laboratories at the age of eleven, the interest that is at once an inspiration and a challenge to every science teacher worth his salt—how can this interest be maintained and extended without work for eager fingers as well as for keen brains? Practical work should lead to the formulation of empirical laws and hypotheses; science taught in this way becomes a systematic study resting on sound and logical foundations. Effective teaching, therefore, demands adequate laboratories and other necessary facilities, adequate laboratory assistance, adequate equipping of the laboratories, and adequate year by year financing of those laboratories. Laboratory accommodation, assistance, equipment and finance—it is my duty this afternoon to attempt some estimate of the present position in the schools under each of these heads. We know that there are shortages, but we have not been aware of what is needed to make them good.

Early in the present decade, it became obvious that the country would soon be needing more scientists and technicians than were likely to be available, and, moreover, that with the measures in hand, universities and technical colleges would eventually be able to offer places to more potential scientists and technologists than the schools were likely to supply. Industry therefore began to give attention to the position in the schools, and in November, 1955, the Industrial Fund for the Advancement of Scientific Education in Schools was established. Its object, as announced, was to give financial assistance by way of capital grants for building, expanding, modernizing and equipping science buildings. The Fund was directed only, and purposely, to the independent and direct-grant schools because, to quote, ' these are schools which cannot receive assistance from public funds for capital works, as opposed to the maintained schools which are the concern of the Government and the local education authorities.' Altogether, 187 boys' and girls' independent and direct-grant schools are stated to have received grants for the purchase of apparatus. The total amount of money provided by the fund is about £3½ million. It is my good fortune, as a member of the staff of the Department of Education of Cambridge University, to visit the science departments of many independent and direct-grant schools, where in almost every case my ears are gladdened by the sound of concrete mixers at work, and my eyes by the sight of new science buildings arising, not all to the same pattern, but variously and excellently designed for their purpose. In these schools there is an atmosphere of stimulation and invigoration among both pupils and staff. Science in the sixth form is no longer second best to classical and modern studies. As well as the independent and direct-grant schools, the whole country owes a great debt of gratitude to the sponsors of the Industrial Fund.

I am not saying that everything is now well with the independent schools, that they have no more problems. They face two very difficult problems of personnel. First, they have to find more science teachers who will man the new laboratories and educate the increasing number of science pupils, especially in the sixth form. Secondly, if the laboratories are to be properly maintained, they require a greater staff of laboratory technicians. Also, things are never static, new needs will develop, and the laboratories that so adequately fulfil present requirements, laboratories which are adequate in 1958, will be found to be totally inadequate to meet the changing needs of, say, 1968. Nevertheless, a great deal has been done, and one part of the educational system is, scientifically speaking, in good heart.

What of the maintained schools? My best information about them—indeed, my only comprehensive information—is contained in the results of a questionnaire issued in May, 1957, to all schools of grammar type, including direct-grant and independent schools. The questionnaire was sponsored by four—or, perhaps I should say, seven—associations keenly interested in science education, namely, the Science Masters' Association, the Association of Women Science Teachers, the National Union of Teachers, and the Joint Four Secondary Associations. The object of the questionnaire was to discover whether laboratory accommodation, technicians, and equipment in grammar schools are adequate for their purpose. In order to formulate the questions, and to collate the replies, a Joint Committee representing all the Associations concerned was formed, and I have had the honour of being the chairman of that Committee. The questionnaire was issued in May, 1957; the replies, which referred to the academic or financial year 1956-57, were returned during the following term. The report of the Committee is written, but has not yet appeared in print, so any figures I give are quoted in advance of publication, and any deductions I make from them are entirely my own affair, and not the responsibility of the Committee. I have, however, no knowledge of any differences of opinion between my colleagues and myself.

Forms were sent to over 2,000 grammar schools, or schools with grammar-type streams, including direct-grant and independent schools. Useful replies were received from over 500 schools—that is, about a quarter of the total. For statistical purposes, we had to discard multilateral, bilateral and technical schools, new schools which have not yet developed up to a sixth form, and schools with less than a two-form entry. The statistics therefore refer to about 440 schools, maintained, independent, and direct-grant. These schools are spread all over the country with a bias, perhaps, towards the London area.

One question asked schools to state the number of laboratories they possessed, classified as ' large,' ' medium ' and ' small.' A 'large' laboratory is one of the standard Ministry size of 960 square feet or over. Schools were also asked to state the number of lecture or demonstration rooms that they possessed. Having received these replies we were, of course, faced with the question, ' what standards of adequacy do we adopt?' Rather than attempt to devise standards of our own, it seemed better to take the standards of other responsible bodies—namely, the Ministry of Education and the Industrial Fund, to which I have already referred. The Industrial Fund standard is, of course, considerably higher than that of the Ministry. Thus, for two-form entry schools, the Assessors to the Fund decided that the minimum needs of a school with a reasonable amount of sixth form work in chemistry and physics alone are two elementary and two advanced laboratories, four in all. Biology would require two more rooms, so we get a total of six rooms for a two-stream school. The Ministry has different standards for boys' and girls' schools. Thus, for a two-form entry, a boys' or mixed school is held to require four laboratories, and a girls' school only three, as compared with six given by the Industrial Fund standard.

Corresponding figures are obtainable for three-form and four-form entry schools.

When the results of the questionnaire are compared with these two standards, we find that of the 373 maintained grammar schools, only 44 per cent reach the Ministry standard and practically none— one school only, to be precise—attains the Industrial Fund standard. Over 75 per cent of the independent and direct-grant schools reach the Ministry standard, and some 15 per cent the Industrial Fund standard. We must, however, remember that the time of the enquiry, May, 1957, was before many of these schools had brought into use their new Industrial Fund accommodation. By this time next year, the number of independent and direct-grant schools with laboratory provision up to the Industrial Fund standards should be approaching 100 per cent.

The figure I want to emphasize is that less than half of the maintained grammar schools (44 per cent) have laboratory accommodation sufficient by the Ministry of Education's own standards. And, for two reasons, this figure of 44 per cent is likely to be unduly optimistic: first, because, in order to obtain these figures, we have counted all laboratories, large, medium and small, as if they were large laboratories; second, because the Ministry has supposed that girls' and mixed schools should have less laboratory accommodation than boys' schools. If the Ministry ' boys' school figure,' is applied to all schools, boys', girls', and mixed, we find that only 20 per cent of the maintained schools are adequately provided with laboratories.

Information about the provision of rooms ancillary to the science laboratories was also obtained from the questionnaire— that is, preparation rooms, store rooms, balance rooms, and workshops. The situation here is much the same as for the laboratories themselves: that is to say, less than half of the grammar schools are adequately provided.

Science teachers were also asked: ' What additional accommodation (if any) do you consider necessary for the teaching of science in your school?' Less than 10 per cent of the maintained grammar schools considered their science accommodation adequate. A further 16 per cent will have sufficient when new buildings are completed. Some new building is going on. No less than 74 per cent had accommodation considered inadequate, with no new buildings in prospect. The direct-grant girls' schools were equally badly placed. Other direct-grant and indepedent schools were better off, and most of these should soon be adequately provided for. One notices that new physical and biological laboratories seem to be required more frequently than chemical laboratories and there are, in the opinion of the teachers concerned, marked shortages of preparation rooms, store rooms, demonstration rooms and workshops.

Before leaving the subject of laboratory provision, I wish to emphasize once again that practically none of the maintained grammar schools (one only in our sample of 373 such schools) attains the standard of laboratory provision established by the Assessors to the Industrial Fund. By the Ministry's own standards, as published in the *Building Bulletin 2A*, well under half the maintained grammar schools, 44 per cent to be precise, are adequately provided with laboratories, and most of this 44 per cent are, in fact, girls' and mixed schools for which the Ministry has lower standards than for boys' schools. If we reject the hypothesis of inferior scientific provision for girls' and mixed schools, then, measured against the Ministry's own standards for boys' schools, only one-fifth of our sample of 373 maintained schools are adequately provided with laboratories. I do not wish to chide the Ministry for having differing standards for boys', girls' and mixed schools. I suppose this is merely a realistic appreciation of the situation. One cannot but feel, however, that what is not good enough for boys ought not to be good enough for girls.

I am, of course, quoting figures for a random selection of one-quarter of the grammar schools, but we have no reason to suppose that the figures for the whole number would show any different pattern. One of several indications that the maintained schools replying to the questionnaire are not a worse-than-average selection is the fact that they have nearly 13 per cent of their pupils in sixth forms, while Ministry figures published in the official year book for 1957 show that the average enrolment in the sixth forms of all the maintained grammar schools in the country is less than 10 per cent. We have 13 per cent in our sample compared with 10 per cent in the whole group so I think we may safely conclude that the schools answering the questionnaire are not a worse-than-average selection.

One thing is certain; good though the direct-grant and independent schools are, and excellent though their contribution to this

67

country's science and technology may be, only the maintained grammar schools can supply the numbers of scientists and technologists that the country requires. To neglect the maintained grammar schools means complete scientific disaster for this country. The sponsors of the Industrial Fund have pointed the way. One feels that the Ministry and local education authorities must not lag behind.

I turn next to the question of laboratory technicians in schools. Out of 362 maintained grammar schools answering this part of the questionnaire, 92—that is, 25 per cent—have no laboratory assistance at all, 31, or 9 per cent have only part-time help, and 78 (22 per cent) have only one junior assistant. Only 54 (15 per cent) have one senior and one junior assistant (or more), and we can be certain that one senior and one junior assistant is the absolute minimum that can be considered adequate. Therefore, we deduce that at least 85 per cent of the maintained grammar schools are inadequately supplied with laboratory assistance. In fact only the smallest schools can manage with one senior and one junior assistant. If we adopt the standards of the 1955 *Report on Laboratory Technicians,* published by the Science Masters' Association, we find that not a single maintained grammar school for boys reaches the required standard. Things are not much better in direct-grant and independent schools.

I wish to emphasize the importance of an adequate provision of laboratory technicians. They are absolutely essential if the best possible use is to be made of that very scarce commodity, the teacher. In the minds of some local authorities and governing bodies, there still seems to linger the vestigial remnant of the idea that, in being asked to provide a laboratory assistant, they are being asked to spend money in order to do something that science staff ought to do for themselves. One could find many arguments for the provision of laboratory technicians, but even on the economic side, it is obviously absurd to pay a science teacher £1,000 or more per year and then intimate that you expect him to spend his time washing bottles or swabbing benches. I know that the main difficulty is to find technicians who are prepared to enter the schools, in face of the competing claims of industry and the higher wages paid in industrial jobs. Nevertheless I would like to make three suggestions. Much could be done if local authorities will

(1) make provision in their estimates for the employment of

laboratory technicians even if, in particular cases, they are not immediately obtainable;

(2) make certain that the maximum salaries paid to efficient and well-qualified technicians are such that they can regard the job as a life's work, and not merely as a stepping stone to some better paid industrial employment;

(3) ensure that the technicians they employ do, in fact, improve their knowledge and efficiency by means of suitable evening courses in technical colleges, and see to it that increased efficiency so obtained receives its due reward in a higher salary scale.

In other words, the job of laboratory technician in a school should be such that it is an attractive profession for a young man to enter, and one that he will be able to progress in and regard as his life's work.

In making these remarks, I know that several enlightened authorities are, in fact, putting these ideas into effect. In this, as in much else, the need is to bring all authorities and governing bodies up to the same standard of enlightenment as that of the good authorities. Proper provision of laboratory technicians would be a great step forward in raising the status of science teachers and in encouraging more graduates to enter the profession.

Next comes the question of laboratory finance; that is, the means of obtaining the apparatus and equipment. Here we have no recognized standards because no data are available from the Ministry or from any other source suggesting how much a school should spend annually on equipment. To me, at any rate, it seems certain that 10s. yearly for each pupil taking science is the absolute minimum if laboratories are to be efficiently maintained and used, and even this amount is too small in schools with large sixth forms. Out of 337 maintained grammar schools answering this part of the questionnaire, 144—that is, 43 per cent—had less than 8s. per year for each pupil taking science. Science teaching at these schools must be sadly impeded by lack of supplies.

The variation between the best and the worst-provided schools is colossal. At one extreme, an independent boys' school has over £3 per year for each pupil taking science, and one maintained boys' school has 28s. At the other extreme, one boys' maintained grammar school has only 1s. 1d. per pupil per year. No other boys' school has less than 3s. 6d., but 26 girls' schools receive between 1s. 3d. and

3s. 6d. annually for each pupil taking science. Financially, as in other respects, it seems that the girls' schools are, in general, worse off than the boys' schools. All the schools answering the questionnaire are attempting similar work with pupils of similar attainments, and the wide range of expenditure is quite indefensible. The schools with less than 10s. a year—that is, more than half of the grammar schools—are being subjected to conditions that are frustrating and inimical to the work they are called upon to do.

The remedy is obvious. The governing body of every grammar school should make certain that the amounts provided for laboratory expenditure are adequate. This may be difficult, because very often, in the estimates that governors see, laboratory expenditure is not separately presented, but occurs as one item in an omnibus figure including books, stationery, and many other items. It would certainly help if expenditure on laboratories were set forth as a separate item, so that governors could consider it separately and make any necessary recommendations.

Finally I should like to refer to some ' General Comments ' in which 256 schools gave 70 different reasons for the difficulties they faced. The first comment is concerned with another aspect of laboratory finance. Only 44 per cent of maintained grammar schools are allowed to purchase apparatus directly from suppliers. Of the remaining 56 per cent who have to purchase through a county supplies department, one-quarter complain of more or less serious difficulty in obtaining the supplies they require. These difficulties are especially acute in areas where the supply department is not under the control of the Chief Education Officer.

I do not wish to condemn supply departments out of hand. They have their uses, for example, the advantages of bulk purchase and cheaper prices, with stocks more readily available. They should not, however, be used as a means of coercing schools into purchasing different apparatus from that which they require. Among other complaints were the following:

Seventy-nine schools had cramped and crowded accommodation;
Thirteen complained of sharing accommodation; that is, using another school's science laboratories;
Nineteen said that their laboratories were widely separated, in several cases by a mile or more;
Twenty-one complained of laboratories used as form-rooms,

while 16 complained of much science teaching having to be given in classrooms;

Twenty-two complained of having no laboratory assistants, and 48 more complained of poor quality laboratory assistants.

Before leaving the subject of the grammar schools, I should like to remark on the special position of girls' schools as shown by the answers we received. In all respects they are less well provided than boys' schools. One cannot but think that it is in the girls' school that the principal wastage of the nation's potential scientific talent takes place. Although this country could produce greater numbers of male scientists and technologists than at present, the increase in numbers of trained women could be much greater still. I do not accept the conclusion, so frequently put forward, that, in the field of science, women are intrinsically less able and less educable than men. The girls' schools could be a very important source of the increased numbers of scientists required in industry, in Government departments, for teaching, and for other purposes. Every effort should be made to supply the teachers, the laboratories and the equipment which the girls' schools require in order that they may play their proper part—that is, a very large part—in the scientific development of the country.

I cannot end without a few words about the secondary modern schools. So far, I have been talking about schools of the grammar-school type, which are the main source of the nation's supply of scientists and technologists. Indeed, most of this Conference so far has dealt with grammar schools. We must not forget that some 75 per cent of the children of this country go to secondary modern schools or are in comprehensive, bilateral or multilateral schools receiving education of 'secondary modern' type.

We must beware lest in our thinking on this problem we unconsciously begin to think in terms of 25 per cent of highly educated 'alphas,' and 75 per cent of moronic 'gammas.' Seen from a strictly scientific and industrial viewpoint, the secondary modern schools are the main source of our technicians and they provide some technologists; but, more than that, we can be certain that science cannot flourish in this country if three-quarters of the population have no scientific background and no understanding or appreciation of scientific achievements and possibilities.

I am afraid that I cannot attempt to give an overall statistical picture of the position of science teaching in the modern schools, in the same way as I have tried to do for the grammar schools. However, no elaborate questionnaire is needed to discover that these schools have very few sufficiently well qualified science teachers, and that laboratory provision is, on the whole, much worse than in the grammar schools. The amounts available for expenditure on laboratory equipment are, in general, ludicrously small compared even with the low figures I have quoted for the average grammar school. Thus, for example, from figures given by 80 secondary modern members of the Science Masters' Association, the amount received per pupil per year ranges between a minimum of 1s. 9d. and a maximum of 6s., with an average of about 3s. 3d. per pupil for the year.

There is, however, another side to the picture. Many a secondary modern teacher, although trained in subjects other than science, has recognized the fact that, if he does not teach some science, then nobody will, and he has gallantly taken his place before the laboratory blackboard, where his personal qualities of enthusiasm and teaching ability make up for his lack of scientific training. Also, some of the newer schools are well equipped with laboratories, if not with apparatus, and there may be positive attractions in modern school teaching: for example, relative freedom from examinations and more opportunity of trying new teaching methods. On the whole, however, these schools are poorly served in comparison with the grammar schools.

In conclusion, and by way of summary, I want

To congratulate the sponsors of the Industrial Fund on the excellent fillip they have given to science education in the best of our independent and direct-grant schools.

To ask the British Association to exert all the influence it can bring to bear on local authorities and on the Minister of Education in order to raise the standard of laboratory provision in the maintained grammar schools to something approaching that which the independent and direct-grant schools already have, or will shortly attain.

To ask that as far as means are available, special attention be paid to the needs of (a) girls' grammar schools, and (b) secondary modern schools, although I recognize that in both cases the limiting factor will more often be a shortage of teachers rather than a shortage of laboratories. However, if the laboratories are there, the teachers are much more likely to be forthcoming.

Lastly, although I have had to give the facts as I see them, I want to emphasize the danger of too gloomy a picture. Excellent work is being done by the great majority of schools of all types; science teaching in this country is fundamentally sound. Prospects for the future are brighter than ever before—I am thinking now of the young person entering the profession—and science teaching is a matter of national concern, as, indeed, the calling of this Conference shows. Never before, it seems to me, has science teaching been such an encouraging and rewarding profession for a young man or young woman to enter.

A great task lies ahead. Not only must we produce more scientists, but, still more important, every future citizen must have an adequate scientific background; science must become a central or ' core ' subject for pupils of all ages. We have the men—we want more. We have the women—we want more. It has been my task this afternoon to ask for the tools—give us the tools, we can do the job!

DISCUSSION

Sir Graham Savage (*Industrial Fund*). During the last two years, it has been my very great privilege to be concerned with efforts on the part of industry to improve the science accommodation of a large number of schools in this country. During that time, I frequently heard the remark ' This is all very good, but what about finding staff? Staffing is really one of our chief troubles.' That is my reason for intervening in this discussion today.

The independent and direct-grant schools with which I have been dealing are those which are getting first choice from the available pool of science teachers. Their conditions of work are good, their accommodation is now adequate, and they have improved their stock of apparatus. The consequence is that the bulk of the maintained schools will find it increasingly difficult to recruit staff so long as the number of science teachers is limited. So the staffing problem is very much in my mind at this time.

I have been very interested in the plans of the Minister of Defence for reducing the number of officers in the services and offering agreeable terms on which a certain number should be prematurely retired. I feel sure that some of these ex-regular commissioned officers would be a very useful source of supply. I do not know the exact figures—I do not suppose anybody knows them accurately—but between 2,000 and 3,000 regular officers are coming out of the services within the next three years or thereabouts.

The Ministry of Labour took a hand at once, as was right and proper, to make it easy for these officers to find employment. Their ages range from 32 to 50, but they are mainly between 35 and 45. They are mature people. When the Minister of Labour set up the committee to ease their passage from military to civilian life, I felt at once that people like myself should help at the receiving end, because here were some cohorts of recruits who might come to the help of our rather hard-pressed army, and particularly in the field of science teaching.

In the main, the regular forces today are an army of technicians. Their interests lie mainly on the science and mathematical side rather than on that of the humanities. Let me take particularly the Navy since I know its situation best. Most of the naval officers prematurely retired will have come through Dartmouth and there never was a better equipped or better school than Dartmouth for teaching mathematics and physics. Two years at sea as midshipmen followed, still under very definite instruction, and then they went to Greenwich from which, after a year's work in the application of science and mathematics to service needs, they were appointed sub-lieutenants at the age of 21 or thereabouts. There are more or less comparable conditions in the Army and in the Air Force.

All officers in the course of their work spend much of their time in instruction. A very senior officer in the Air Force told me that until the last year or two, 75 per cent of his time was employed in giving instruction. We have, therefore, a body of men to whom teaching is not something new. We also have, in the main, a body of men whose interests are in the field in which we are concerned: science and mathematics.

I wondered how they would be absorbed, and I sketched out

in my mind what I would do myself if it were my job. My mind went back to the years after 1946, when the Ministry of Education set up an imaginative scheme of recruitment for much larger numbers. Many thousands of men were then released from the Forces and the Ministry set up 50 or 60 of its own emergency training colleges. Surely here is a case for emergency training colleges on a much smaller scale but of a more highly specialized nature. In the main, these officers are good at mathematics and physics but not by any means so good at chemistry. Their chemistry could be brought up to a reasonable standard to enable them to teach the subject at least to the lower forms of grammar schools, thereby releasing others for more advanced work. At the same time they could be given an opportunity of adapting their knowledge of physics and mathematics to the needs of school teaching. That is what I rather hoped would happen.

I asked a colleague at the Ministry whether anything of the kind was in prospect, but was sorry to learn that the Ministry had no such scheme in mind. I am rather hoping that views may be expressed collectively at this Conference to make sure that a great opportunity is not missed.

I gather that what is happening is this. Some 500 individuals have already written to the Ministry and made enquiries about the possibility of entering the teaching profession. Do not let us attach too much importance to the number of 500—I expect that everybody who is coming out of the services has about half a dozen irons in the fire—but those 500 have applied for information, and others will doubtless do so.

When they make a firm application, they are referred to a committee of four principals of training colleges, who, if they consider them suitable, recommend them for admission to two-year colleges. In other words, they are being treated as non-graduates and being trained as non-graduates. My view is that these people are essentially of the same standing as graduates. They can be recognized as such under the Burnham Scale, they get the Burnham graduate allowance if they do become teachers and it seems to me that we are likely to lose a large number of potential recruits if the only mode of entry to the teaching profession is by way of the ordinary training college if and when they can secure admission.

The training college course is a two-year one, but the man of 35 or 45 with a family does not want to spend two years on preparation, nor do I think he needs it. One year is probably as much as he can stand. Furthermore, he will be mixing with people 20 years his junior, and that in itself may be understandably distasteful to an officer who may recently have been commanding a ship or a squadron of aircraft.

I feel very disappointed that some more imaginative scheme has not been set up. I have been seeking further information and I gather that at the moment only 70 of these officers have been interviewed for admission to two-year training college courses, and of these only nine have been accepted for a one-year course. The rest, apparently, will have to take a two-year course. Moreover, many will not be able to start until September, 1959. I confess that I should like to have seen special courses for them possibly at intervals of three months. Doubtless, this would cost money, but not an extravagant sum and, if the country is seized of the urgency of the situation, as most of us here are, the country will agree that the money must be found.

I hope that the Ministry of Education may perhaps hear some whisper of this matter, and I see my friend the Permanent Secretary is not very far away. I hope he will not take it unkindly if I suggest that the present method of handling this problem is likely to lose us several hundred recruits. A more imaginative approach —a real operation—is necessary to recruit these officers as they leave the Forces and to deliver them to us as reinforcements when their training courses are completed.

MR W. J. LANGFORD (*Head Master, Battersea Grammar School*). In view of something I shall say presently, I would mention that I am a mathematician. None of us can now be in any doubt about our problem, if ever we were before. Its seriousness has been clearly revealed during the course of today's proceedings.

Dr Boulind urged us not to take too gloomy a view. That is, of course, wise advice. We must never get to the stage where we believe that the outlook is so gloomy as to be hopeless. On the other hand, I can assure him that he has not exaggerated, because earlier surveys in more restricted areas—one, for example, in

Derbyshire, Leicestershire and Nottinghamshire, another in Devon and Cornwall and yet a third in Wales, carried out by the head and assistant masters in those areas—underline only too strongly the figures which he gave.

I had the privilege of serving on the committee over which Dr Boulind presided when they wrote the report of which he has been speaking. One thing that puzzles me is why he only had about a 25 per cent response to his questionnaire. It surely must have been clear to those in the schools that a group of responsible people were trying to do something valuable and important and that they really needed information. I suspect that some head masters put it in the waste paper basket, having already heard of Sir Eric James's conservation law, but I cannot believe that that accounts for all the missing three-quarters.

With regard to buildings, I believe I am right in saying that a former Minister let it be known at the time of the launching of the Industrial Fund that he would take care of the provision of laboratories for the maintained grammar schools. Now is certainly the time for the Ministry of Education to come out into the open with their own programme. It is, fortunately, a matter of money, and money only. If that money is forthcoming, I see no reason why the local education authorities and the voluntary aided schools will not be able to deal with their accommodation problems.

On the question of technicians, I can give a useful example from personal experience. My senior technician came to us straight from the Air Force immediately after the war, without even a matriculation qualification. In the twelve years since then, he has covered the whole university range by part-time study and last July he got second-class honours in physiology at the University of London. His admirable persistence has been rewarded, but he was given the encouragement of the heads of the three departments teaching science in my school, who helped him at every stage. That is the kind of positive contribution to the technician problem that should be considered when we are thinking of the question of recruitment.

On the question of money for material Dr Boulind has given the figures. The only comment I feel able to make is to quote the price of a packet of cigarettes, or two visits to the cinema,

77

as the amount of money that is available annually for each science pupil in a very great number of our schools.

In speaking of the supply of teachers, I would like to comment about the situation in Russia. The White Paper compared our supply figures with those for the United States and for Soviet Russia. The Russian schools have now established a compulsory seven-year teaching programme and are well on the way to ten years' schooling for every child within the Union.

Russia makes the claim that there is no teacher problem throughout the whole of the Soviet Union. I was privileged to go on the United Kingdom delegation to the International Bureau of Education Conference at Geneva in 1956, when that particular claim was made. When we asked how it was that they had no problem of teacher recruitment, we were simply told, ' We saw the need coming, and we planned for it.' The result of that planning was that in 1955, 80 per cent of the graduates from the universities in the Soviet Union were directed into teaching. No wonder they solved their problem!

I am firmly in agreement with Dr Barton's suggestion that the only way in which we can solve our problem is by, in some measure, controlling the appointments which are available. It is entirely foreign to our way of life, it would ruin the whole spirit of teaching within our schools if ever any attempt were made to direct an individual into a particular kind of work. But I believe firmly that there are many men and women whose specialist qualifications are not being used to the best advantage in the service of the country and its young people. I am convinced that the only way to solve the problem is, as Dr Barton suggests, in some way to consider the allocation of appointments which are available.

We have talked about teachers and about the buildings. What about the other factor, those who are being taught? I am convinced that the best of our young people, boys and girls, bear comparison for quality with their contemporaries in any country in the world. I think we have a sufficient number of teachers at the moment—the future is a little more obscure—to safeguard the best of our young people, but I am certain that we have not got nearly enough to give the great majority of our young people what they deserve, that is an adequate scientific education throughout the whole of their school life.

I should like to make this suggestion. It seems to me an easy request to make to the heads of the schools throughout the country that they should give an indication of the number of boys and girls who in two years' time, if they remained at school and went through the Advanced level course, would, at the age of approximately 18, be able to read an honours degree in science or mathematics, a general degree, or a specialist course in science or mathematics in a training college. I am firmly convinced that that could be done now with a fair amount of accuracy, to provide us with figures on which we could base calculations for 1960.

Then, we should turn to the universities, the training colleges and the technical colleges to make provision for those young people in 1960 and onwards. It may well mean a complete overhaul of provisions like maintenance allowances from local authorities to safeguard the sixth-form course. It may mean an extension of the provision of county major awards, perhaps even of State scholarships. It will give the universities time to think about the possibilities of expansion, although I am one who believes firmly that we must not expand too greatly the science and mathematics faculties in our existing universities. I believe that if we make them too large, we shall inevitably drag down the standard of the best, and that is something to be avoided at all costs.

I am convinced that our national programme of further education is sufficiently flexible to cope with these young people. If we can get a sufficient number of the best of them going on to further education, then there will be some hope of meeting this great need which lies before us in 1970.

Mr K. A. Hooton (*Forest Hill School*). I was very pleased to hear Dr Barton introduce into the discussion this afternoon the sordid subject of money for teachers. It is, of course, something that teachers are not supposed to talk about, but it is nevertheless very important.

Dr Barton quoted something over £500 as the salary of a science master before the war compared with £1,400 today. The £1,400 includes, of course, the highest responsibility allowance (£350) which only a few receive. Before the war, a bar of chocolate cost 2d.; now, a bar of the same size costs 6d. If we multiply just over £500 by three, to discover what the head of a science department ought to have now if his standard is to be the same as before the war, we arrive at a figure of over £1,500.

Since 1938, the level of prices over the whole range of commodities has gone up by at least three times; it has practically doubled since 1947. If we multiply Dr Barton's 1947 figure of £800 by two, that brings us to £1,600.

I do not want to harp on the question of salaries, because I realize that it is not the only thing to be borne in mind concerning teachers, and it is perhaps not even the most important thing, but it is *an* important thing; and if you want to get good-quality teachers into the schools, you must be prepared to think about salaries. If the country wants to attract gold here or money into the banks, it raises the bank rate. If you want more teachers, you have to raise their salaries. It is just as simple as that.

Mr Langford spoke about the need of money for development in schools. Whatever our shade of political opinion, we should all strive to see that education costs are not cut. We should have more money for education, and not less. What we want is almost an advertising campaign. For example, the British Association might go on to expound the arguments in simple figures. That is perhaps not exactly scientific, but it is very effective with the general public. The cost could be shown in relative figures. Last week, for instance, we were told that for 1s. per day per person, Britain could take part in inter-planetary exploration. We want a similar figure to show what it would cost to get ourselves out of this very great danger in our schools. It is a greater danger, perhaps, than we faced during the years of the war. At that time everybody saw that there was a danger of Hitler invading this country; but it is very difficult to convince people that if we do not keep up our supply of scientists we run the risk of becoming, not a second-rate power, but a fifth-rate power.

Mr G. S. Brown (*Head Master, Tewkesbury Grammar School*). Dr Boulind has told us that the Ministry of Education's standard for laboratory accommodation is much below that which is now being applied in independent schools, and he has made it clear that very few maintained schools reach even the Ministry's standard. Yet we have heard from another speaker that the former

Minister of Education promised that the maintained schools should not lag behind. In actual fact, the efforts of local authorities have been frustrated.

I can quote my own case. In common with several other grammar schools in Gloucestershire, we were recently promised a new laboratory, but by direction of the Ministry the project has had to be postponed. Something that this Conference could do would be to urge that plans like ours should go forward without delay.

In considering the supply of teachers Dr Barton did not think that the method of sharing teachers was of much use. He told us, however, about the terrifying number of 1,100 vacancies in science staffs. While we are waiting for teachers to be trained in universities the present situation is likely to become worse. During that period sharing may provide a temporary measure of relief.

There is another temporary device, which has not been mentioned today but which, I think, could be tried. I suggest that industry might release some of its scientists for part-time teaching. My suggestion is based on experience because by the kindness of the National Coal Board and Dr Bronowski, two research physicists regularly visit Tewkesbury Grammar School and teach physics in the sixth form. Their help is very valuable. I understand that a similar scheme is in operation in the North West making use of research scientists from Manchester University.

SESSION III

MEETING THE NEED

Mr M. G. Bennett, Chairman

I should like to say one or two things as one of the honorary officers of the British Association.

We are delighted that our venture in laying on this Conference has received so much support. You are very welcome and you can rest assured that all suggestions which may arise for positive action will be noted carefully. We shall presently, by our machinery, gather together these suggestions and do everything we possibly can to use them.

You are probably all aware of some of what we are proposing in the programmes for our Annual Meeting at Glasgow this year; we have a very extensive and enlarged programme of lectures, demonstrations and exhibitions which should help to interest young people in science. We have also a student membership of the Association. Nevertheless, we shall continue to look for subjects like today's which are suitable for conferences between our annual meetings where matters of pressing public importance relating to science can be discussed.

I also draw attention to the fact that we have recently set up a panel of 80 lecturers who are available to any of you who want lecturers on any branch of science. These people have offered their services which will cover all aspects of science, even those subjects, like the history and philosophy of science, on which comment was made yesterday. I think that the panel will gradually grow, and we hope you will make use of our speakers.

Inquiries about the lecture scheme should be addressed to the offices of the British Association. It may save some confusion if I remind you that these offices will shortly be moved to 18 Adam Street, Adelphi, London, W.C.2.

Yesterday we had a series of papers and discussions on what

might be called the statement of the problem. These papers and discussions cannot be regulated within definite boundaries, but it is fair to say that, broadly speaking, yesterday was devoted to a statement of the problems whereas this morning we are endeavouring to consider the remedies—how the problems can be met. We shall deal with these remedies under two heads— the supply of the teachers and the supply of the facilities.

The teachers come from two sources, the universities and the teachers' training colleges. We shall, therefore, here from both of these sources something of their problems and future prospects. The university point of view will be represented by Professor Dame Kathleen Lonsdale and that of the training colleges by Dr Chesterman. When we come to consider the provision of facilities, by which we mean not only laboratories and equipment but non-teaching staff and technicians, we have to turn to the local education authorities who are responsible for resources and finance. We shall hear first from Dr Hill who has many other qualifications to be heard, but will on this occasion speak mainly as a representative member of a county borough authority, and then from Dr Lawrence who is the Chief Education Officer of a county with both urban and rural problems.

SCIENCE TEACHERS—THE ROLE OF THE UNIVERSITIES

Dame Kathleen Lonsdale

In preparing this talk I was torn between the alternatives of speaking about what the universities could do with their present resources, but don't; and what they might do with suitably increased resources. I have decided to try to do both.

As with the other speakers, my first instinct, as a scientist, has been to obtain sufficient reliable data. I have attempted to find out what proportion of university graduates, in different scientific disciplines and of either sex, adopt school teaching as a career. My statistics are incomplete, partly because the records kept by the various universities are themselves incomplete. Many past students do not inform their universities about their careers or their changes of career, and do not fill in forms that are sent to them. In that they seem not to differ from some head masters and head mistresses. The University Grants Committee receives annual returns from all universities, but I am told that the results of this information have not so far been published, because of the unavoidable deficiencies in the data supplied.

Nevertheless certain deductions can be made from the available figures, and I am greatly indebted to the Registrars and Appointments Officers who have helped me with information and comments, which come from eleven universities and refer to periods covering from two to ten years.

First of all, the number of men graduating in science is much greater than that of women. Proportions vary between about 3:1 for Glasgow and Edinburgh and about 8:1 for Cambridge and Bangor. This disproportion is particularly high in physics and chemistry, where the general average last year was about 13 men to each woman honours graduate; less in mathematics, with a ratio of under 4:1; and least in the biological sciences, with a ratio of about three men to two women.

Secondly, the percentage of science graduates adopting school teaching as a career is much higher for women than for men. Total percentages in different universities vary between 10 per cent and 25 per cent for men, and between 29 per cent and 60 per cent for women. The 60 per cent, however, is based on inadequate numbers. Oxford, Cambridge, University College London and the University College of North Staffordshire all had a 10 to 11 per cent average production of male science teachers over a three- or four-year period. Manchester University and University College, London, tied with the lowest percentage—29 per cent—of women science teachers, while Edinburgh, Oxford and Cambridge came next with 33, 34 and 35 per cent respectively. Sheffield, Glasgow and Edinburgh had the highest percentage total production—27 per cent—of science teachers of both sexes.

In spite of this preference of women graduates for teaching, the absolute numbers of women science teachers are much less than the numbers of men, simply because there are far fewer women science graduates. It may be suggested that the lower percentage for men is due to National Service, but it appears, from the information I am given, that very few take up school teaching *after* National Service.

The absolute numbers of those studying the physical sciences are about four times those studying the biological sciences, but relatively fewer physicists or chemists choose to teach, and the supply of teachers of the physical sciences is less than twice that of teachers of the biological sciences. The percentage of mathematicians who teach is comparatively high, but their absolute number is only three-quarters of that of the physicists and chemists together. Some figures given to me by Mr Langford show that in 949 grammar schools of all types, there are 539 mathematics teachers who have no recognized qualification in mathematics.

In general, the percentage of teachers recently produced is higher for the lower-class honours degrees and for the General B.Sc. degrees, but an exception to this rule occurred in the years 1956 and 1957 when teaching with a good degree carried indefinite deferment from National Service, whereas other non-military posts did not. One or two Registrars called my attention to this fact and pointed out that in these years there were even a few men with post-graduate degrees who switched over from research to teaching, a rather unusual phenomenon. In other words, men do not usually take up teaching after National Service, but they do take it up as an alternative to National Service. It may be that if and when National Service comes to an end, some of these may leave the teaching profession, but at least the lesson is clear: men will go into teaching if there is sufficient inducement, positive or negative, to do so, and I do not believe that these men will make worse teachers than those who go into teaching because jobs are more easily come by there than elsewhere.

There is considerable variation between universities in respect of absolute numbers and proportions, but not in respect of the trends that I have mentioned. These facts, therefore, may point to some directions in which improvement in the supply of science teachers may be assisted by the universities, or by the University Grants Committee and the Government, working through the universities.

The first and most obvious fact is that more women must be attracted to science as a career, since they are potentially a better source of teachers. We have heard from Dr Boulind that in all respects the girls' schools are less well equipped for science than the boys' schools. Only a few of the independent girls' schools benefited at all from the very generous Industrial Fund. This lack of facilities must be remedied if good teachers, not necessarily women, of course, are to be attracted to girls' schools, and girls are to be attracted to science. The same applies to the science departments in the relatively few teaching colleges for women in the universities.

If it is worth while having such special women's colleges at all, then their science departments should be generously equipped and well-staffed. There might also be, at the mixed colleges, a considerable number of entrance science scholarships reserved specifically for women. Incidentally, I should like to correct one statement made by Miss Huxstep. At least as far as London University is concerned, there is no fixed proportion of men and women entrants. The only reason that the number of women admitted to science courses is so low is that so few are sufficiently well qualified. If more were up to standard, the proportions would change. We must somehow break the vicious circle of few women scientists, few women teachers: few women teachers, few women scientists; and we can break it by accepting, at least for the time being, young women entrants who have no more than the minimum entrance qualifications. Many of these young women scientists will not enter the teaching profession, but it is clear that a large proportion probably would do so.

Many of them will get married; and why not? That will be an excellent thing, as long as these intelligent, scientifically-minded women are positively encouraged to have children. I am never happy when I hear of the large number of childless married teachers. Quite a number of our men students are married; often their wives are supporting them. I look forward to the day when our universities have crêches attached to them and young mothers can continue their university training if they so wish, knowing that they can enjoy their babies at the same time, at least as much as does the young society woman who employs a nannie, or the young working mother who puts her babies in a municipal nursery.

The young girl who is being asked to take up a career in science must not be allowed to believe that this will automatically debar her from early marriage and motherhood. Why should it? It didn't debar me: quite the reverse! But it ought to be made easier than it was for my husband and me. What is needed is a science-minded public, and to get that you must begin with science-minded parents. When my own children became of school age, I was quite naturally intensely interested in the teaching, and particularly the science teaching, they were given, and that interest will extend to my grandchildren.

I was glad that Miss Almond mentioned the Reading University refresher course for older married women, who, having brought up a family to the age of independence, would like to begin or renew a career in teaching, but who realize that their knowledge is out of date. There might well be special bursaries or special income tax concessions for these older trainees, if the universities and the Government will play ball. After all, we find training courses and jobs for men and women demobilized at the end of a war. Why should there not be opportunities and encouragement for women whose service for the nation has taken the form of bearing and rearing children, and who have 20 or 30 more years of useful working life?

A further suggestion, which came from Dr Edward Teller during his testimony before the U.S. Senate's Preparedness

Investigating Subcommittee, a committee which met within a few hours of the launching of the first Soviet earth satellite, is that a system might be worked out by which university scientists, and scientists from industry, could each give, say, upwards of 20 hours a year of their time to talk to children in primary and secondary schools. Some of us already do this on the occasion of school Speech Days, for which I can assure you that a titled and married woman scientist is in great demand! If only I were glamorous as well as being a ' mother of three ' and a grandmother I daresay my recruitment value would go up enormously.

As you have heard from our Chairman, the British Association is now enlarging its activities to do the same sort of thing, believing that this is one of the ways in which a lasting interest in science can be roused or stimulated; and it is also forming area committees for the continuous supply of science lectures to the public throughout the year. In some of these area committees, the extra-mural boards of local universities are playing a considerable part.

All this education of the public is necessary if we are to have not only the supply of science students in the universities but the jobs to give them when they are qualified, bearing in mind that only a percentage will want to teach. It is of no use asking girls to take science degrees if there is nothing but school teaching to offer them when they are qualified; and with some notable exceptions, of course, industry is not yet eager to employ women scientists.

I am quite sure that we shall not get a supply of women science teachers merely by exhortation, as the Government White Paper on *Technical Education* appears to suggest. If it is felt that special inducements are required, then these will have to be organized and financed.

It seems to me that the remainder of my time might well be divided into four parts: first, conditions of entry to the universities; secondly, courses offered by the universities; thirdly, guidance given to students in respect of subsequent careers; and fourthly, limitations imposed on the universities by existing conditions of space, staff and finance.

First of all, I am sure that we need to remind ourselves that the present shortage of science teachers in schools is an accumulated deficit. Once that deficit has been made good, the increase in the demand is likely to be small compared with the increase in the requirements of industry. Any expedients asked of the universities to meet the present demand must, therefore, be either temporary or of a nature that will be permanently useful in other ways.

The subject of the procedure for the selection of undergraduate students is one with which both schools and universities are very much concerned. It was discussed at length at last year's Home Universities Conference convened by the Committee of Vice-Chancellors and Principals. The sad fact is that in spite of, or because of, the horribly elaborate selection procedures, which are not only inefficient for their purpose but also a nightmare both to the schools and to the universities, the Kelsall Report showed that 2,000 reasonably qualified applicants did not obtain a university place even after two successive applications in 1955 and 1956, and yet apparently there were also something like 2,000 places unfilled in 1956. In addition, as Mr Kelsall pointed out in the discussion at the Home Universities Conference, there must have been a great body of potential university material among those who did not apply.

Sir Solly Zuckerman spoke yesterday about cutting off the tail of the entry and thus raising university standards. My colleagues who for years past have had to choose 40 out of upwards of 400 chemistry applicants wish that they knew how to tell which is the tail. Entrance examination, head master's or head mistress's report, 'A' level or scholarship success, intelligence test or simply the fact that they are the children of the right parents; none of these is infallible. At present there is little, if any, correlation between the order in which students are placed at entry and their subsequent performance. Some are late developers and do much better at college than they ever did at school; others for one reason or another never live up to their early promise. Perhaps it is just as well that no one university quite knows how to skim the cream off the milk.

Nevertheless one cannot but agree with the Vice-Chancellor of the University of Liverpool when he says that sooner or later a conference of responsible admitting authorities will have to be called together to hammer out, in consultation with the schools, something like a uniform, though not inflexible, procedure. This

Conference may wish to endorse that suggestion. What must not be done, however, is to impose a career condition on entrants. Entrance scholarships ought not to carry with them the obligation to teach. At the same time if an applicant has a genuine concern to teach, he or she should be given every opportunity to acquire the requisite qualifications. In particular, the absence of Advanced level G.C.E. science ought not be an absolute bar to a science career at the university level.

Universities will certainly wish to maintain high entrance standards and will probably continue to use some form of examination for the purpose; but evidence of intelligence is surely more important at this stage than a detailed knowledge of nuclear physics and there might well be more experiments in first-year courses which cater for the intelligent but uninformed, as well as for those who are quite capable of specializing but who do not wish to specialize. This brings me to the question of courses.

In the first place, I simply do not agree with Dr Barton that teaching has been neglected in the universities for the past 40 years. My experience is that most university teachers take their jobs very seriously indeed. Of course the science faculties have emphasized the importance of research, because research is the very life-blood of science; and if research were to be neglected, science teaching would not become more inspired and inspiring, it would become lifeless. Even science teaching in schools, if it is to have any value as a part of genuine education, must partake of the nature of research. I agree, however, that too many students are taken through intensely specialized courses which are not what they need, and for which they are not suited.

I am absolutely convinced that a highly specialized training is not necessarily the best training either for school teaching or for much scientific research work of a semi-routine type, or indeed for original research work in borderline sciences such as my own, where a working knowledge of several sciences is far more important than a very detailed knowledge of one. Specialization can and should follow a first degree, but only for those students who need it and can profit by it. What I am suggesting is that instead of spending up to three years in sixth form specialization at school it would be far better to have a younger age level of entry to the university, at a lower level of factual cramming than at present. Some schools, I know, would not like this because their science staff prefer advanced teaching, and because grants and allowances depend on the number of sixth form scholars. But it is partly the increase in the sixth forms that has aggravated the shortage of science teachers.

It is also claimed that the third year in the sixth is necessary in order to teach young people to work on their own. This, however, they can and should learn in the first year at the university itself, if they have not already learned it. In any case, it is not supposed that a uniform pattern can be impressed on all schools and all universities. I think that the general trend to stay at school longer and longer is one to resist.

Let us suppose, therefore, that entrance qualifications are changed so that most students come up to the university at about 17 years of age. Then I suggest that every science student should be required to take a course in two, three or even four subjects, which would lead to a first degree. If every student took this general degree, universities could rid themselves, once and for all, of the idea that a general science course is mainly a convenient dustbin for their selection mistakes. It would be a sieve, but not a dustbin.

Those for whom a general knowledge of science is sufficient —and this would include some men and women proposing to become industrialists, administrators or, I hope, politicians—need go no further. The general degree could be followed, however, by a variety of post-graduate courses. One could be a one-year teaching-training course; another could be a two-year specialized course in one of the sciences, equivalent to the present two final years of a special degree, but minus all those students for whom such a course is not suitable; and another could be a combined course of lectures and of research in one of the borderline sciences such as my own subject of crystallography. These could lead to a higher degree by examination and dissertation or thesis. Or it should be possible to switch from the science faculty and take a course in languages, literature, law, engineering, medicine, economics and so on. Incidentally, I am quite sure that obligatory Latin should disappear from entry requirements. It is a relic of the Middle Ages.

Some such pattern as this exists, of course, in certain universities already. I should like to see it adopted far more widely. It would maintain high university levels, and indeed raise them, for a five-year course on a broad base would turn out better specialists and provide more scope than we have now. It would provide a sensible and honourable way out of the university at an intermediate stage; and by knocking off one or two years from the sixth form it would relieve the pressure on schools, without unduly delaying the entry of the trained man or woman to their careers. It would also give the students the opportunity of considering their future careers after a sufficient experience of university life but before the need to do so becomes really urgent.

The present practice in my own college is that several months before their final examination students are interviewed and snapped up by representatives of industrial firms. As far as I know they are seldom, if ever, given the chance to hear the case for school teaching and if they become teachers it is in spite of and not because of the recruitment system adopted. If the present shortage is to be remedied quickly, we need something like an all-out recruiting drive. Compulsion, no! But the right kind of 'direction' is simply a perfectly legitimate form of advertising. I am glad to hear that a meeting of the Committee of Vice-Chancellors with heads of schools will shortly discuss the possibility of regular visits of distinguished head masters and science masters to the universities to put the claims of teaching before science undergraduates. But if the choice were between a further two years' grind for a special degree and a one-year teacher-training course I rather fancy that there would be more teachers, and they would be just as good.

There is no point, however, in making plans that involve a longer student course for a considerably greater number of students unless university facilities are expanded. The science intake is limited by laboratory space and equipment, and by the available staff. If, as is suggested, the country needs twice as many scientists, it must pay for them. At present the money provided by the Treasury through the University Grants Committee is not enough to run science departments on a modern basis, especially when import duties imposed by the Board of Trade, on the arbitrary decision of non-scientist bureaucrats, take away with one hand what the U.G.C. has given with the other. The result is that senior university people have to spend an absurdly large proportion of their time endlessly seeking benefactors. I speak with some bitterness, because I happen to dislike begging. We are indeed grateful to our benefactors, but this is not an economic use of scientific manpower.

On the other hand, of every £1 spent on research today 15s. comes out of the taxpayer's pocket; but out of that 15s., 12s. is spent on so-called 'defence' research. The result of this obsession with defence is two-fold. The first is that many parents and many young people look at modern science as something powerful but essentially devilish. They are repelled by it, and I am not surprised at that. The second is that science for peaceful, constructive purposes is hampered and starved of support.

Perhaps the most important role of the universities of all nations is to produce thinking men and women who will no longer tolerate this anachronistic and suicidal prostitution of the world's wealth and of scientific talent. Then we might get some new universities in which bold experiments could be tried, and we might get administrators who would realize that science teachers could be available if the nation wanted them enough to pay for them.

SCIENCE TEACHERS—THE ROLE OF TEACHERS' TRAINING COLLEGES

Dr D. R. Chesterman

I hope to show how training colleges during the last few years have been meeting the shortage of science teachers in secondary modern schools, and how from emergency measures a longer term solution has emerged which will help both modern and grammar schools. Other types of science training will be described, including the four-year course. Finally, the position of primary schools will be briefly examined and some possible developments in junior school training described.

During the last five years the output of science teachers from training colleges has increased year by year, and very greatly so since 1955. This output should both continue to grow and to improve in quality, for a number of reasons. It is a combined operation, depending on both schools and colleges, and this year the standard and quality of science candidates who have come up for interview, at least to London training colleges, has shown a striking improvement. This is partly caused by the change in call-up for National Service, but since it is shown by both boys and girls it clearly reflects as well the successful efforts that are being made in the science sixth forms of grammar schools.

Meanwhile, during these five years, the maintenance grants of students have been substantially improved, so that they can now better afford to stay at college for the extra time that the better science courses demand. Further, we have the promise of a three-year course for all training college students in 1960. The extra year will be of incalculable value to every student, but perhaps especially to the scientist who, needing so much time for practical work, has faced an almost impossible task within the confines of a two-year course. Finally, and for a number of reasons, entry to training colleges will become more selective in the next few years.

Training colleges prepare students for teaching in primary schools—infant and junior—and secondary schools—secondary

94

modern in the main—after a course which for most of them still lasts only two years. Courses vary in different colleges but always include three main divisions: first, the education course—the professional theory and practice, that is; secondly, the curriculum courses—providing directly usable teaching matter and method in a number of different subjects; thirdly, one or more main subjects, specially chosen and studied for the student's personal education, and usually for secondary teachers offered as teaching subjects. There is, too, a course in English language.

The demands made on any science teacher, primary or secondary, are considerable, and the scanty curriculum courses are quite inadequate as a training to teach science unless the student already has a very wide and substantial knowledge of the subject. The main subjects, particularly if only one is studied, will reach a much higher level than a curriculum course, but in the two years only a fifth or less of the students' total college time can be spared for their main subject. Even if the student has come from school with a good sixth form science course behind him, he cannot, on such a two-year course, reach a level which will fit him to be a satisfactory specialist science teacher.

In the past, national policy concerning training colleges has been far too much like that of Jonah's whale. Jonah, the prophet, you will remember, was a very large man and, when swallowed, he gave the whale a bad time. It was then that the whale made his famous utterance—'Oh for small prophets and quick returns!' A long-term education policy of quick returns can be disastrous.

Before describing courses that are considered satisfactory it is well to consider the needs of the schools. I shall take first secondary modern schools. The need for good specialist science teaching in these schools is, I think, a double one. The vocational aspect may well affect a substantial and increasing number of boys and girls, for secondary modern schools have developed greatly during the last few years. In particular, as we were reminded yesterday, the brighter children are being much more adequately catered for, and there are now many courses leading to the G.C.E. In all but name many of the schools have become bilateral, with the equivalent of a secondary technical or grammar stream for these cleverer children. Given adequate science teaching we can, I believe, expect from these schools an important flow of valuable young people who can now make use of our increased provision of technical colleges and become qualified for a variety of scientific vocations.

It is quite certain that the eleven-plus examination misses some potential scientists, whose gifts are not always associated with verbal ability and mental agility. Such children deserve the same kind of opportunities they would or should have had in grammar schools— good laboratories and well-qualified teachers. In any case, the country cannot afford to neglect any source of scientists or technicians at whatever grade.

For the remaining children in the secondary modern schools, representing three-quarters and more of all the children of their age group, there can be no question of a vocation requiring a good knowledge of science. But the case that has been made out for science as a cultural subject applies to children of all kinds and includes those of limited ability. The stimulation of curiosity and wonder at natural phenomena, and the recognition of science as a major human activity, should find a place in the education of all children.

This, then, is the double challenge that training colleges are facing in the secondary modern schools, and they have been meeting it by what are frankly emergency measures. At the same time their task has been made more difficult since some of the best science teachers leaving training colleges have, understandably enough, obtained posts in grammar schools.

Secondary modern schools were, of course, evolved as a result of the 1944 Education Act, and thus few of them are more than a dozen years old. The condition of science teaching in many of them during that time has been deplorable, largely owing to the lack of suitably qualified staff. Often the building programme has outstripped the supply of science teachers, and excellent laboratories have been in charge of staff with virtually no knowledge of science.

To meet the immediate crisis, training colleges which themselves had suitable lecturing staff and laboratories have been engaged in a scheme of supplementary courses financed and initiated by the Ministry of Education.

Supplementary courses cover an academic year, and have been available for many years in a variety of subjects, including general science, at various selected training colleges, to qualified teachers —deferred courses for those actually engaged in teaching and continuous courses for students who have just qualified but not started full-time teaching. Unfortunately it was until recently almost impossible to attract candidates to take the supplementary science courses. Continuous candidates found the training college maintenance grants most unsatisfactory and could not afford to stay on for another year. At the same time the existing regulations made it almost impossible for a practising teacher attending a course to be seconded on full salary.

The maintenance grants were greatly improved at Easter 1955, and it was then also made easily possible for selected teachers to attend a year's course on full pay. The figures speak for themselves: in 1953, the national output was 9; in 1954, 11; in 1955, 29; in 1956, 102; in 1957, 163. Because of the crisis we accepted students at a much lower level of attainment than we would have considered for other subjects. As an example, one woman teacher, in charge of science in a big secondary school, had never used a chemical balance. Numerous men were found to be in charge of school science on the strength of an R.A.F. short course in radar, and nothing else. Some of the emergency trained men teaching science had no qualification of any kind at all in their subject.

Fortunately, what these teachers lacked in attainment they made up for in keenness and ability to work at college. These 300-odd science teachers—from recent supplementary courses—will now have a useful contribution to make in modern schools. It is to be hoped, though, that they will be given an opportunity of an additional course in a few years' time.

A more permanent solution has recently developed from the supplementary courses. It will be realized that few of the supplementary students had taken science as a main subject when at college. Clearly, a great deal would be gained if it were known in advance that a student starting on a two-year course with science as a main subject would stay on for a supplementary year in science. The whole three years could be integrated, general curriculum subjects now made unnecessary could be shed, and far more time could be devoted to science.

This great step forward was made possible in 1955 when the Ministry of Education invited certain of the better-equipped training colleges to start what was called—since only the Government could initiate a three-year course—a two-plus-one integrated course.

97

There were a few restrictions, but near enough two-plus-one made three and enabled us to obtain in advance most valuable experience of the three-year course in action before its universal introduction in 1960. We still have much to learn about the best way of using the three years, but in science at least a definite pattern is emerging. This science three-year course is suitable only for secondary teachers, owing to the heavy demands of what are virtually three main subjects taken together—chemistry, physics and biology, with some mathematics as well.

The importance of this integrated two-plus-one course is being recognized fairly generally and recruitment is rapidly increasing. In 1955 there were 32 candidates; in 1956, 93; and in 1957, 153.

If a student's standard at entry to such a course is at 'A' level in three subjects, a very useful standard indeed should be reached at the end of three years. The course, though varying in different colleges, is a wide one, covering usually the full range of physical and biological science, and obviously includes teaching method. Without gearing it to any particular examination, it should be possible for numbers of the better students to take such examinations as Part I B.Sc. General of London University in their stride and to be well on their way to Part II by the end of the course.

It would greatly help if better incentives and opportunities were given to young men and women with these partial qualifications to go on studying while teaching, using the three years more or less as a springboard. Technical colleges and universities would be doing a great service to such teachers if they could provide not only suitable evening classes but also part-time day and vacation courses, so that their qualifications could be completed without undue strain.

At the present time it is certain that many of these three-year trained scientists will obtain posts in grammar schools, teaching junior and middle school forms. Few universities offer opportunities for studying both the physical and biological branches of science together as does this course. It must be remembered, too, that the products are all trained teachers, experienced in working with children.

A small number of training colleges offer four-year courses in science, which have superseded the old three-year concurrent degree and diploma course. At Goldsmiths' College, after lean years when few candidates came forward, we now take 25-30 entrants each year.

After three years spent in working for the London University B.Sc. General degree, a further year is spent in professional training, including a term's teaching practice, and the course ends with the examination for the Postgraduate Certificate in Education. A course of this kind could, with a few important modifications, become almost the perfect training for all secondary teaching apart from the advanced work in grammar schools.

My first point of criticism is that General degree regulations in science are usually conceived in terms of a number of separate subjects. Some of these, particularly mathematics, are so demanding that even a good candidate will be left with no time during the course to read and to reflect to any extent on the meaning of science as a whole, and to study its historical and philosophical background. Without any lowering of total standards, it should be possible to prune some of the separate subject requirements, and to put in their place a compulsory paper concerned with science as a human activity. The cultural purpose of our science teaching would, I think, be encouraged by a suitable examination.

Secondly, it is unfortunate that the immense importance to the future teacher of doing at least a small independent investigation at the frontiers of knowledge has been so completely overlooked in most degree examinations. Thus a degree requirement might well be the production of evidence of a piece of simple research or investigation. A degree conceived in this way for teachers would certainly guide them in the right direction.

Students taking the training college four-year course have certain advantages. Their lecturers are all experienced in the methods of school teaching and so are able to present their subjects in a way which includes the classroom angle as well as the adult academic approach. The students are thus not unprepared for the fourth year of professional training. When qualified they usually obtain posts in grammar schools or comprehensive schools.

In primary schools, even at the top end of the junior school, there is usually very little specialist work and the class teacher is expected to teach all the subjects in the curriculum. Primary school children cover the full range of abilities, for ' creaming ' comes only after the 11-plus. This means that, apart from the boys and girls who go to preparatory and public schools, all the potential scientists and technologists will pass through the primary school. It is thus of immense importance that the scientific interests of all primary school children should be treated with encouragement and understanding. With a wrong attitude on the part of the teacher it is possible for them to develop prejudices against a scientific subject, prejudices which may persist for years.

What is perhaps not generally realized is the early age at which children now seriously become interested in science—perhaps from the stimulus of television. From about the age of six they will start bringing to school clear and definite questions about such things as ZETA, rockets and space travel—questions by no means easy to answer clearly and definitely in a way appropriate to their age. At six of course, they will have emotional interest in live plants and animals. But the compelling interest for most of them at that age, as we have found by experiment, is in scientific apparatus—magnets, simple electrical working models, lenses and mirrors and so on. They want to know how they work and the strange thing is that it is often from such experiences that their reading and writing first develop.

With the right sort of guidance this kind of interest will develop in the junior school, and will probably extend to natural history—to stars, planets, volcanoes, as well as to the stock-in-trade of our technical age, atomic energy, X-rays, jet engines and so on. Bees, pollen and germinating beans now have only a limited interest. Children still, thank heavens, exhibit the attitudes of curiosity and wonder, but clearly these are now being particularly directed to physical phenomena.

All this puts a big extra responsibility on to the training colleges. Children's curiosity should be satisfied in a way appropriate to their understanding and interests. Moreover, curiosity and wonder are the motive force behind the child's learning. Yet it would be very difficult, even after we have a general three-year course, to expect every junior teacher to add natural science as an extra teaching subject to the already lengthy list. The following suggestions show one way of meeting the difficulty.

We must not lose sight of the fact that our overriding task in the training colleges is to produce educated men and women. When the general three-year course starts in 1960 there seems to be an overwhelming argument for including a basic course in science as part of the personal education of students—not, of course as a teaching subject for all students. This should help teachers to form a positive and understanding attitude to science, and would then solve one of the junior school problems.

But in addition each junior school should have on its staff at least one teacher with a broad training in science, capable of acting as a consultant to the other teachers. It is this teacher who should have the task of dealing with the barrage of questions involving physical science. This can be done by such means as one-man brains trusts on Friday afternoons and personal guidance in clubs to interested children from all classes. Even with such a teacher on the staff few junior schools would probably want to undertake more formal science teaching than is comprised in a course of natural history based on topics. Systematic physical science is not suitable for junior schools and if attempted often causes children to lose interest in the subject at the secondary stage.

Because of the birthrate bulge, training colleges have been substantially increasing their output of secondary teachers, and the number of new junior teachers with main subject science qualifications has shown no increase, being roughly stationary. However, the total number of students taking general or physical sciences as a main subject increased from 392 in 1953 to 681 in 1957, and of those taking biology from 709 to 852. A substantially increased number of secondary school teachers are therefore going out with at least some science qualification.

An additional and important source of science teachers is to be found in certain training colleges, which have special facilities for main subject courses in rural science, with a few students taking a supplementary course in rural studies. This branch of our work will undoubtedly develop after 1960, and make its own increasing contribution.

It is perhaps beyond the scope of this paper to discuss technical education, but it may be pointed out that three training colleges are concerned with this work, and it will be remembered that a recent circular reported a rapid forthcoming increase in the number of such teachers to be trained.

All the expansion which has been described has been done with few increases in staff. The total science teaching strength in training colleges is now slightly less than it was in 1956. In some colleges, therefore, the science staff are becoming greatly overworked. The difficulty of staff recruitment is well known and it is complicated by the fact that one really needs extra allowances for scientists to attract good enough men and women into training college work. There will be further expense, for though the Ministry of Education has been generous with grants to certain colleges for extending laboratory accommodation, it is likely that much more money will be needed for us to extend further.

The colleges have achieved a great deal in a very short time, under the spur of an emergency, embracing not only the actual shortage of scientists but equally the birthrate bulge and the large classes in schools. They are encouraged by the contribution the grammar schools are already making with their sixth forms. They now need the assurance of adequate time and money, for good teachers cannot be obtained on the cheap.

The three-year science course promises the beginning of more time, and the brave words in a recent circular from the National Advisory Council on additional courses, supplementary to the three-year course, leads me to a further hope—that a four-year science course will before long become the accepted form of training for teaching science in secondary schools of all kinds. This Conference of the British Association may yet persuade those who control the coffers, both in the Government and in industry, that the education of teachers is worth paying for.

DISCUSSION

MR DAVID GOULDSTONE (*Wandsworth School*). Despite what has been said about the training colleges, I think that they are failing to give their science students sufficient incentive to acquire further qualifications. The attainments on entry of students at training colleges often include two subjects taken at Advanced level after two years of sixth-form work. In some cases they have the minimum qualification for entry to university, but universities now require far more than minimum qualifications before they accept a student. If such students after two years of science in training college want later to proceed to a university degree I do not know of any university which will give any credit whatever for the work done in the training college period. Taking the teacher's certificate in some subjects is therefore a blind alley. The student has to start again from scratch if he wants to graduate.

He should of course be encouraged to contemplate graduation. I attended a London training college (not Goldsmiths') and I found that in many cases men were discouraged from taking any sort of extra qualification such as another 'A' level subject which would afterwards help them to proceed to a degree. But one looks at the science students at Birkbeck College and sees that very nearly 50 per cent of them are teachers, most of whom have had to start again from scratch and to go back and take the Intermediate.

May I make one remark about supplementary courses? I should have thought that it was as important for a teacher to be allowed a one-year supplementary course to complete an honours degree as it was for him to take a course in rural biology. At the moment that is not possible. No local education authority in the country will give a grant to enable him to do it. If he has had a grant for a two years' course, he cannot receive a grant for a degree course. There is no alternative but part-time study.

My last comment is on research in schools. It is often said that school teachers have no time to do any research, and I know that it is difficult in view of the timetable. But I think that more scientists might be encouraged to take up teaching if they were allowed time in school for a little of their own research.

Miss L. H. Higson (*Secretary, Association of Women Science Teachers*). The Association of Women Science Teachers contains 1,600 members, chiefly in Great Britain and Northern Ireland but also sprinkled all over the world.

I want to make a plea for those older women teachers—and they amount to at least 40 per cent—who are single women and who have had a vocation for teaching. Their heart and soul are in their school work and it comes first in their lives. We have heard from Miss Huxstep that this type of science teacher is likely to become scarce in the next few years. Many of these women are now about the age of 50 and my experience is that some of them are very tired. I want to advocate that they should be given a sabbatical year in which to do whatever they like. Some of them may prefer to spend the year in study whereas others might travel or take a complete rest. They would all come back renewed and refreshed and ready to go on with their work until the age of retirement.

In our Association we have heard of a number of break-downs many of which, we think, could have been prevented by a little rest. I expect that the Ministry of Education will have figures, and it would be interesting to compare the number of break-downs among science teachers with the number among those who are teaching other subjects. I suggest this because the science teacher is on the go the whole of the day, and very often in the middle of the day she has dinner and other duties from which, in my opinion, she could be relieved. If she is to run her laboratory continuously she needs at least a half-hour's rest in the middle of the day. We must conserve the teachers we have.

This conservation raises psychological problems. I should have liked a psychologist to speak to us today to say what qualities are necessary to produce a good science teacher or a good scientist and to give us some idea of what he considers to be the percentage of the population which has those qualities. I know that Dame Kathleen has said that she can take only 40 out of 400 applicants, which means rejecting 360. Those 360 are not completely rejected, because they may get into other universities or into technical colleges. Most of these young people apply to at least six colleges. The selection system needs simplification but we have not yet acquired the necessary data about numbers and standards. It would be possible to expand our universities and to admit all serious applicants. But then we should either have to turn students out at the end of the first year, or lower the quality of our degrees. Either course would be undesirable and we should try to reduce the difficulties by careful study of our national brainpower.

I should like to mention what my Association are doing for secondary modern schools. About ten years ago we invited the Science Masters' Association, the Association of Teachers in Training Colleges and Departments of Education and, a little later, the London Association of Science Teachers, to co-operate with us on a joint committee to discover what we should do for secondary modern schools.

Our first efforts were to run conferences, and for about four years we had about two meetings a year for secondary modern science teachers. After that, people with more resources provided larger and more elaborate conferences and we decided that this was not our line of work any longer. We have since been producing pamphlets, and have so far brought out six of them, called *Science Teaching Techniques,* published by John Murray at 3s. each. They contain articles and short contributions from practising teachers on how to approach their subject in the best way, and sales have been quite encouraging. We should be grateful now for suggestions from any quarter for the future work of this sub-committee.

Finally, I want to thank the British Association for all the inspiration it has given to science teachers over the years. I remember the time about 25 years ago when only about half a dozen women science teachers attended the Annual Meetings. The number has increased until now it is more like 100. We go back inspired and renewed in mind as a result of these meetings. We owe a very great debt of gratitude to the British Association.

Mr B. S. Braithwaite (*Education Officer, East Sussex*). Miss Huxstep said yesterday, rather sadly I thought, that in girls' grammar schools the teaching staff fell into two distinct groups, young teachers in their first jobs, and the bulk of the staff who were over 40 and perhaps even over 50. We have to remember how that came about. When the girls' grammar schools were recruiting staffs in the 1920's and 1930's, there was a very different supply situation. About a million men had been killed in the first world war and their women contemporaries had remained unmarried. I think that is the simple explanation of Miss Huxstep's point.

Dame Kathleen Lonsdale said that graduates in physics and chemistry were not becoming teachers. That is not only true of university graduates in these subjects but it is also true of students in technical colleges who are reading for external degrees or professional diplomas. The other day at lunch in a technical college I noticed a table full of gentlemen who did not look like members of the staff, nor like a "snoop" of H.M.I.s I asked the principal who they were and he said, ' They represent industrial firms and they are here to collect bodies.' I said, ' But it is only February. What about the examinations next June and July? ' He replied, ' That does not bother them at all. They are recruiting now.' I said, ' But they may pick people who will fail their examinations.' He said, ' Indeed they may. Last year we had a girl who failed in everything she took, but she got a job, and she is now doing research with an important corporation.'

We have to remember that many of us in this room chose our careers in the thirties when the teaching profession offered several inducements: long holidays, good pay, superannuation and, above all, security. The last three of those—good pay, superannuation and security—have all been overtaken by other employers, and we are left only with the holidays. We are now trying to recruit against that background. The negative inducement of exemption from military service which Dame Kathleen mentioned has now been removed and we have to rely on positive inducements. If I wanted to be very controversial, I should say that there is only one real positive inducement and that is more pay.

While one has to admit that in the last two or three years appreciably more graduates have been coming into teaching than in any period since the war, unfortunately they are not science graduates. I could suggest that the only remedy is additional and special pay for science graduate teaching. If this differentiation is thought to be unacceptable I would turn and ask Dame Kathleen whether some of the medical staff in her own university and college are not paid more than their colleagues in other faculties.

SCIENCE FACILITIES—THE ROLE OF LOCAL EDUCATION AUTHORITIES

Dr J. W. F. Hill

I hope I shall not be thought to be introducing a discordant note if I mention a word which could not be expected to play much part in our deliberations. So far it has not been mentioned by anyone, and I marvel at my own temerity in mentioning it. It is the word ' economy.' Local authorities, like the rest of us, live in a cold hard world in which economy matters, and they are constantly receiving exhortations to try practising it from the Chancellor of the Exchequer, the Ministry of Education, who sent us their *Circular 334* on 27th January last, from industrialists (including those who employ scientists and would like to employ more), and from ratepayers large and small.

We all know that the electorate, whether national or local, is sometimes disposed to will the end but not to will the means, and if this Conference can create a better-informed public opinion and so shift the pressure on local authorities from the ' economy ' quarter to a better one, it will have done a valuable public service. My own experience leads me to believe that the ratepayers who, after all, in another capacity are parents, are more easily convinced about the value of education than they are about the value of some other public services.

I appear to be one of the few entirely lay members of this Conference. Having been a member of a local authority and a local education committee for over twenty-five years, I have had it pretty well brought home to me that local authorities have many other duties besides those of education. In the immediate post-war years we should not have been heard to say that science in schools was more important than housing, and even today it would not be easy to place all the different claims on local authorities in any precise order of importance.

The purpose of my preamble is to provide the perspective in which local authorities have to see their problems. It is certainly not to offer any sort of defence or apology. Indeed, I shall go on to claim that local authorities have a good record in the development of the education services, and that marked progress has been made since the war in provision for science in schools. The framework of educational administration is known to everyone here, and all I can do is to present a few pieces of evidence to show not only that local education authorities do not need to be persuaded of the importance of education but also that they are very much alive to the national need with which the Conference is concerned. I should be the last to suggest that there is any ground for complacency, but it would be a mistake, into which I am sure we shall not fall here, to belittle what has been done and what is being done. We can, however, measure the size of the problem which remains.

Hard cash is one of the measures of the progress made, and in order to be as concrete as possible I should like to give some details of the educational building programme for 1958-59. The programme was compiled following the Ministry's letter inviting proposals for extensions to schools containing a substantial number of pupils over the age of fifteen, the proposals being designed to provide adequate facilities for the teaching of mathematics and science. The details which I have are compiled from replies to an inquiry sent out to county borough local education authorities. Out of 83 county boroughs 79 replied. They have been analysed for me by the kindness of Mr Russell, the Chief Education Officer for Birmingham.

Apart from three proposals for transferred schools and one proposal for a new school which are not included in these figures, 31 proposals for extensions of existing premises were submitted by 21 authorities.

The estimated value of 29 of them, two not yet having been assessed, is about £1,226,000. Of the 31 proposals, 21 were included by the Ministry in major building programmes for 1958-59, their estimated value being £863,000, plus a sum to be determined later for one of the more substantial applications. Four additional proposals, estimated to cost £134,000, were included in reserve programmes. Thus, in all, apart from proposals for new and transferred schools, it appears that county borough authorities alone asked for extensions to the value of about £1¼ million, and the

Ministry agreed to some five-sixths of these proposals, to the value of over £1 million. For one year this is good going. No doubt the county authorities could show similar results.

During the morning Sir Gilbert Flemming has been good enough to hand me a copy of the answer to a question asked in the House of Commons yesterday, which I should like to read to you. Mr Owen asked the Minister how many grammar schools were not yet equipped with science laboratories up to the standard required by his Department and what steps were being taken to remedy the shortage to meet the sixth form numbers which would arise with the bulge. The Minister replied:

' I cannot say how many grammar schools lack adequate science laboratories but projects costing some £2 million have been included in the 1958-59 building programme for additional science accommodation for grammar and technical schools. I have recently invited local education authorities to submit proposals for further improvements of this kind so that I can consider their inclusion in the 1959-60 building programme.

In two of the replies to my circular giving nil returns it was stated that additional facilities for science had been provided during the past few years, and this is probably true for most authorities. It is clear that all of them are fully aware of the need for provision of this kind and that they have been doing what they can for some time.

There has been a great deal of consultation with specialists, including those who will have to teach in new rooms and laboratories, on problems of design and lay-out, and on the supply of furniture, apparatus and equipment. As a result, satisfactory provision for science has been made in new schools and accommodation in older schools has been brought up to date wherever possible, under minor building programmes or as part of extension schemes made necessary by the increase in numbers of pupils in the schools. Programmes since the war and up to and including the 1957-58 programme have provided £14·8 million for accommodation, and £3 million for equipment in 4,500 laboratories. The Ministry tell me that including the figures for 1958-59 the totals become £19 million for accommodation and £4 million for equipment.

It can honestly be claimed, therefore, that both the Ministry of Education and local authorities are alive to the importance of providing adequate accommodation and equipment in their schools and that they are doing all they can within the regulations to provide satisfactory laboratories and other facilities for work up to the highest standards likely to be required of the schools.

That is my first piece of evidence. May I now call attention to the significant increase in assistance to students at universities and technical colleges. The Ministry's annual reports show that the increase in the number of State Scholarships over the last ten years, for which the figures have been published, has been matched by an even larger increase in the much more numerous local education authority awards. The figures are so striking that I must ask you to bear with me while I read them. In 1947, the number of State Scholarships was 750; in 1956, 2,249; State Supplemental Scholarships rose in the same period from 789 to 1,575, and Technical State Scholarships from 59 to 150. The total of Ministry awards therefore rose from 1,598 to 3,974. In the same period, local education authority awards to students in universities and university colleges rose from 3,705 to 13,640; and to those in technical colleges from 3,798 to 9,085: the total of awards being 7,503 in 1947 and 22,725 in 1956. The Ministry's awards have increased in number by 149 per cent and the local education authority awards have been increased in number by 203 per cent. As the number of university places grows there will of course be still further substantial expansion.

I have already referred to Ministry of Education *Circular No. 334* of 27th January. It includes a passage on awards, and authorities are reminded of the importance of discrimination in selection. Though this has particular reference to courses outside the normal range of studies at universities and technical colleges, the mere inclusion of a reference to awards in a circular on educational expenditure will tend to lead to some, perhaps a slight, slowing down in the rate of expansion.

Within a month of the issue of the *Circular* came the announcement by the Chancellor of the Exchequer about student numbers in the universities which are expected to increase from about 84,000 in 1956 to about 124,000 in the mid-sixties. Provision is being made for large non-recurrent grants to universities for the building and equipment of laboratories. Perhaps we may infer that not much is expected or even intended from the *Circular*, and that it belongs to the class of what lawyers call ' general words.' But if any admonition is to go from this Conference on the subject, I venture to suggest that it should be addressed to the Minister of Education. I should like to pay a tribute to the courage of the Permanent Secretary, who has been sitting at the front throughout this Conference to receive the shafts which may be aimed at him by successive speakers. He will understand that they are received by him solely as agent for the Minister!

These university awards relate to arts subjects as well as to science, but the Ministry's annual reports make it clear that the schools have responded to the call for more scientists and technologists. Roughly speaking, in 1938 the numbers taking Advanced level G.C.E. in the arts and sciences were equal; now we have 60 per cent science to 40 per cent arts; and soon it will be two-thirds to one-third.

At the other end of the university process the recruitment of graduates to teach mathematics and science is beginning to improve. The intake of mathematics and science graduates to university departments of education has grown from 627 in 1955-56 to 719 in 1957-58. There was a small drop in the intervening year, but these figures are higher than those for preceding years. The experience of at least one university is that quality, in terms of degree class, is also beginning to improve; one-half of the scientists and mathematicians have either first or second class honours degrees. Yet there is still talk of ' the flight from mathematics since 1945.' Since mathematics is the language of science that is a grave matter.

These trends have, no doubt, been encouraged by the new Burnham Reports, negotiated by the local authority associations through the Authorities' Panel on the Burnham Committee, which, by giving greatly improved salaries to senior subject teachers, have done something to make teachers' salaries comparable with those offered in industry. As a result of successive Burnham increases, a four-year-trained assistant master with a good honours degree, and receiving a Grade D allowance as head of department, can now reach a maximum salary, including allowance, of £1,425, as against a possible maximum of £685 in 1947.

Moreover, there has been a considerable rise in the number

of posts carrying additional allowances in each school apart from departmental headships. In the area of one large local education authority there are 180 posts carrying additional allowances of various sizes for mathematics and science. Whether we have gone far enough to compete with the offers of industry or whether there should be special scales for scientists, I do not know. Any moves in this direction would raise as many problems as they would solve, and I cannot think that the proposals which Dr Barton made yesterday are likely to be acceptable in this country, because it is very difficult to argue that they bear no relation to the unpopular war-time expedient of the direction of labour.

The increase in numbers of training college students taking main courses in science and mathematics has been dealt with by other speakers, but I want to claim that the local education authorities have played their part in bringing about the very large increase in the number of supplementary courses. They have made it possible by seconding serving teachers to these courses in spite of the difficulties which the secondments impose on the schools. We may presently look for an improvement in the quality of science teaching in primary and secondary modern schools.

There is a natural tendency to think chiefly of the work of grammar and technical schools in the production of scientists; but some people well qualified to judge think there is a great potential in the other secondary schools, and that some of the pupils in them might make a very useful contribution to industry, not perhaps at the higher levels but in other ways which are just as necessary to production. After all, we need a large number of technicians as well as scientists and technologists.

Although I am concerned to emphasize the record of local education authorities in the schools, even this brief review of what is being done would not be complete without a reference to the technical colleges which the local education authorities administer. There are about 500 technical or commercial establishments in England and Wales varying from large colleges of technology, mostly in London and the county boroughs, to small technical institutes. Most of their courses are vocational, but more advanced and less specialized work is carried out at the regional colleges and at the recently designated Colleges of Advanced

Technology. There are at present eight Colleges of Advanced Technology, and two more, at Newcastle and Bristol, may soon be added to the list. These colleges, and a few of the regional colleges, offer courses leading to the newly established Diploma in Technology. Altogether, 1,360 students are at present studying for the Diploma, and it is to be hoped that sixth-formers from grammar schools will in the future come to regard the Diploma for what it is—a qualification of university degree standard.

It is clear that we have not yet decided how many girls can find a career in science. In the past we have sometimes assumed that laboratories in girls' schools are not very important. The vague feeling that girls are unlikely to be good at science is rooted in social prejudice which ought to be abolished. There must be much unused scientific talent among them, and I have been much interested to find among engineers of my acquaintance a willingness to admit that there is scope for girls not only in light industry but in the laboratories, at the drawing board and in calculating work. The numbers of boys and girls taking G.C.E. in English, history and French are roughly equal. In mathematics only about one in nine, in physics one in seven, and in chemistry one in six, are girls. Of these small numbers some of the girls are in mixed schools. In these next few years when it will be very difficult to get a place at a university, girls taking science will have a greatly improved chance of getting in, a consideration which might usefully be put before them.

All the developments which I have mentioned and those proposed by others will require very much more money. This brings me to a point which may be highly unpopular, but at this Conference we are afraid of neither fact nor opinion and I should be less than honest if I did not deal with it, and the Conference would be less than realistic if they did not consider it.

You all know that there is to be a change in the financial relationship between the Ministry of Education and local authorities. The Local Government Bill proposes to replace the existing percentage grant by a block grant. It would be an abuse of the hospitality of this Association to use this platform to say whether I think the new grant system will be good or bad. Whether we like it or not, the Local Government Bill is expected to complete its Committee stage in the House of Commons this month and

I have no doubt that it will appear on the Statute Book without material change in the next few months.

We must not delude ourselves that an alternative Government will abolish the system, although they might revise the formula. I think we have to accept the fact that the new formula will take effect next year and we shall have to operate it at least for a trial period, after which it will be judged by results.

I know that the proposed change in the grant system has aroused widespread apprehension among many people who are devoted to education, but I do not share those apprehensions. I have sufficient faith in the local authorities to believe that their sense of responsibility and their genuine concern for education will ensure that the opportunities open to children in school will not suffer but will continue to improve.

If the British Association should decide to take steps to create or enlarge an enlightened public opinion on the need for science in schools, this is a good time to do it. It would help the Ministry—though I have no authority to speak for them—it would help local authorities and it would help the cause of education and of science in schools if the Association encouraged a campaign of publicity and propaganda in order to 'educate our masters.'

SCIENCE FACILITIES—THE ROLE OF LOCAL EDUCATION AUTHORITIES

Dr B. E. Lawrence

South Kensington is surely a very appropriate place for a meeting concerned with the teaching of science in schools. If this Conference had been held at the turn of the century South Kensington would have been equally appropriate, but there would have been no representative of local education authorities because there were no local education authorities, and you would not have been called upon to listen to a Chief Education Officer because there were none of them either. Not only were there no L.E.A.s but there were then comparatively few secondary schools: the making of more secondary schools and the evolution of new forms of secondary education have been the great work of local education authorities and of the Ministry of Education in this 20th century.

During the 55 years that local education authorities have existed they have, in co-operation with the Board and then the Ministry of Education, brought almost to fruition a system of secondary education for all. I say 'almost' because it is quite clear that there is still a 'rump' to be dealt with, and it is always the last ditch which is the most difficult. But we are within sight of a complete system of secondary education, and I think that local education authorities and the Board and the Ministry can claim a great deal of credit for what has been done. The contrast with the 19th century, when there was much talk and not very much action, has been very marked, and particularly in the last 40 years the growth of facilities for secondary education can only be described as prodigious. The modern schools are almost entirely local authority schools; so are the technical schools and the majority of the grammar schools; and new types of school are beginning to appear.

I think it is probably true that, despite all the grumbles we hear, the needs of individual children in this country are now assessed more carefully and supplied more adequately than they have ever been before. Science is not mentioned in the Education Act, but we can say in regard to science, as much as to other aspects of education, that the local education authorities and their staffs have been able to arrange that more of the right children are with the right teacher in the right place at the right time. And we have retained the English method of leaving it to the school to see that they are doing the right things.

I think that the needs of the community have had much less care in assessment than the needs of the individual. One of the consequences of that lack of care is the manifest shortage of skilled manpower and womanpower of several kinds, including teachers. The shortage of science and mathematics teachers threatens, over the next few years at least, to delay the great progress in providing secondary education to which I have referred.

Science is of course only one part of education and whatever strengthens the whole strengthens the part. What have local education authorities done to sustain and strengthen the system of secondary education which they administer?

They have been trying to encourage a longer and more effective school life in all types of secondary school. They have had some success in reducing wastage at the sixth-form level, although too many pupils still leave at 16 when they could profit greatly by more advanced studies. In particular we have been reminded several times that it is necessary that more girls should remain longer at school. In this matter, of course, authorities help by way of maintenance grants for pupils, but maintenance grants have a relatively small part to play; not very many pupils get them, although they are very important for that minority, and without them some children would certainly be denied their chance of secondary education.

It is of greater consequence that the sums made available to schools for the purchase of equipment and books should be adequate. I think that authorities are recognizing that those allowances should be greatly increased for the older pupils so that the appropriate furniture, materials and equipment can be made available. Local authorities also help to provide for activities such as school visits which supplement the work of the school, and draw children's attention to the outside world in which they are growing up.

116

Another section of school life which is receiving more attention is the building up of libraries. Many school libraries are still not as large as we should like them to be; but county authorities can and do supplement the individual library provision of their schools by the service which they also provide as library authorities. Recent developments have made it possible for schools to draw at regular intervals on the resources of the very large public libraries. That is a contribution which large authorities in particular can make to their schools, to give them the benefit of more ample resources than could be provided by individual school libraries.

Before I come more specifically to science, I want to emphasize a point which Dr Hill made—that every local education authority is also an authority for other services, such as health, highways, welfare, housing, all of which make calls on its resources. I am a little inclined to follow yesterday's example of Sir Eric James and to propound not the principle of the conservation of the curriculum but what I might call the law of the conservation of the cake. If you have to share a cake between the Chief Education Officer, the County Medical Officer, the Surveyor, the Children's Officer, the Welfare Officer, the Fire Officer and others, then if the Chief Education Officer requires a larger share, at least one of the others must have a smaller share. Because education is so large a service it already gets the biggest share of the cake; and the other claimants will be very unhappy if their slices have to be cut even smaller to give more to the one who already has the largest.

We who plead for more resources for education not only have to convince our education committees that the things we want are good things which ought to be provided with the minimum of delay, but we have also to convince our finance committees that the things we want are more desirable and more necessary than the things which are wanted by other people who have a claim on local authority finance.

Next, we have to recognize a number of competing claims on capital resources of the local education authority itself. The clamant demand for more new primary school places is now declining, but primary school building has by no means finished. Every time there is a new housing estate, even though there are no more children in the local authority's area as a whole, there is a need for a new

117

primary school; and there will still be primary school building in my county and many others in the next few years.

A great many old school buildings—and many buildings built over a century ago are still in use—need alteration and improvement; they cannot all be replaced. We have built many new secondary schools and extended old ones. Some new special schools and new technical schools are now appearing and we plan new libraries. It is therefore important to realize that the demand for the improvement of facilities for science, whether in new blocks of laboratories or as part of an extension scheme, has to be weighed with and sometimes against the demands of other educational services. I think that it is unrealistic, for example, to think that all the deficiencies in school laboratories will be made up in a few years.

We could no doubt deal quickly with the science needs of our grammar and our technical schools if they were the only problem; but they have already had a very large share of the new laboratory building which has been mentioned, and there is a very big and indeed much larger deficiency of laboratories in modern schools. As the size of our programmes remains under very strict control, it is clear that the amount which can be allowed for science provision in any one year must be determined in the light of pressures of many other kinds. In these matters the job of the Chief Education Officer is very largely that of keeping a balance between all the various calls which are made on his authority's purse.

Let us look more closely at the claims for more science teaching in schools. I suppose that potentially the biggest of them is the demand that some study of science is to be a part of everybody's education. This implies that all secondary schools, modern as well as grammar and technical, must have qualified staff and facilities by way of lecture rooms, laboratories, preparation rooms, greenhouses and so on. This is a major demand which certainly cannot be dealt with rapidly. It must be looked on as a long-term proposal. A good deal has been said too about the special needs of girls' schools and about the fact that the proportion of girls taking science at school is too low. The facilities provided for many of the older girls' schools are very much inferior to what we provide nowadays and improvements will make a call on resources for several years to come. Again, we want a higher proportion taking science at all levels, which also implies extended facilities.

The third demand arises because more boys and girls are staying at school to the age of 17, 18 or 19 so that the size of the sixth forms has recently been increasing by more than 5 per cent each year. At the same time there is an increase in the proportion of these enlarged sixth forms taking science.

I hope that you will forgive me for mentioning another factor which will cause demands, the large age group which is just beginning to leave the primary schools. In 1958 most secondary schools will have a much larger complement of children than they have ever had before, and the pressure on these schools will grow for several years. There will be some overcrowding, which will affect the teaching of sciences as of other subjects, and in my opinion there will be extreme difficulty in keeping the schools as well staffed as they are at present.

When one looks at these five reasons for growth in the next few years, one cannot escape the conclusion that it is unrealistic to expect local authority schools, or anybody else's schools, to deal simultaneously and successfully with all the claims which will be made on them in that period. I am afraid that it must be recognized that in some cases secondary school classes will be larger. Again, it is inevitable that in some schools the time given to teaching science will be cut. Where there is a clash between the needs of sixth formers and the needs of children lower in the school, many head masters and head mistresses will feel that the needs of the sixth formers must be met to the detriment of the other claims, and that the beginning of science for some of the younger people must be delayed. These are rather unpalatable truths, but it would be unrealistic if I did not mention them.

We have faced difficulties of this kind before and, if the birth rates in 1956 and 1957 are anything to go by, we shall be facing them again. But in some ways we are better prepared now than we were before. I recall the period at the beginning of the war when my county, like Gaul, was in three parts, an evacuation area, a reception area and a neutral area. In the reception part of the county we received boys and girls and school parties from the evacuable part of the county and from London. I can think of a well known school in Essex which had two other schools sharing premises with it for a year. At the end of the year we managed to find another home for one of them, but in the meantime they had all managed to carry on somehow. I am not saying that the wartime expedients were good, but I am saying that we have overcome very much greater difficulties of accommodation than we have at the moment or are likely to have. In the years immediately following the war it was almost impossible to get new accommodation or even to replace some of that which had been destroyed; nevertheless we not only got by; we made progress. Now the teachers know that a big bulge is passing through the schools and they are very anxious that the children shall not suffer more than is necessary because of the overcrowding. They will carry on and get us over our difficulties, because there is no alternative.

But although school staff will meet the present difficulties and overcome them, they will do so more readily if they feel that they are temporary and that permanent solutions of the accommodation problems are being found. For that reason local education authorities should be encouraged to embark on long-term programmes designed to end the shortages which have accumulated in the years since the war. They should be allowed to do this by planning for a period of years, not year by year as for some time past. Everybody concerned could then know what was intended to replace buildings and to add new accommodation. It would be a great help to all local authorities if they were in a position to say to their staffs: 'By 1961 or 1962, we shall have to put an end to these conditions.' Perhaps that is over-optimistic, but at any rate it is right to have a plan and to try to work to it.

There are always small things which authorities can do to help their staffs and their children during a time of special difficulty and emergency. Something has been said about appointing laboratory technicians and assistants and providing them with bigger and better preparation rooms in which to work. The Science Masters' Association have done a very good job in the report which they have produced on this subject, and some authorities have already taken steps to improve laboratory service. Dr Boulind's figures show that there is room for a good deal more, but of course we are seeking that sort of staff at a time when there is a marked demand for their labours in many other fields.

I have referred to the improvement of existing facilities through equipment and supplies of textbooks and other aids to teaching. It would be specially helpful if these improvements could come quickly during the next few years when pressure is heaviest. In the past the Ministry of Education have been able to encourage particular developments by offering larger percentage grants. A special grant would be useful now but we have been told that in the future we are not to have the ' carrot ' of the larger percentage grants. There is, however, one ' carrot ' which would be useful, namely the removal of financial limitations on minor capital works. Given more freedom and resources, a much quicker provision of advanced facilities could be expected.

One thing which more authorities could do is to help their teachers to improve their qualifications in science. Not only do specialist teachers need to keep up to date, but more teachers of science are required and in many cases they have to be found from non-specialists. Possibly we might get some from industry, but we shall find more among teachers in the schools who may have at present few paper qualifications for teaching science. Many of them have the ability to go further and to work for a qualification, e.g., at 'A' level, while those who have 'A' level can start to work for a degree. Some authorities select teachers in those two categories and, give them the opportunity of a day's release each week from teaching work during the period in which they are working for their qualifications.

Dr Chesterman said something about teachers who train by third-year courses. That practice has been increasing rapidly in recent years. It can be recommended to local education authorities on its merits, and because it is a quicker and surer method of relieving the teacher shortage than the method of relying on universities to produce more graduates. A supply of teachers from this source can relieve more qualified staff for advanced teaching.

Reference has already been made to the special problems of girls' schools and I want to support the plea made yesterday that we should try to get back into local authorities' schools, full-time or part-time, some of the married women who are capable of teaching science. Some schools would have been completely without science teachers had they not persuaded such people to come in, but many of these women feel that, after years away from teaching, they are very much in need of a refresher course. If special refresher courses, such as that held recently at Reading University, could

J

be provided generally, I believe that we should have a valuable source of womanpower which could be brought into the schools during the critical years when there will be a shortage, despite all emergency measures.

I also want to support what has been said about mathematics. Perhaps it is because I started life as a mathematician that I feel so disturbed about the lack of mathematics teachers at all stages. Mathematics is so much the language of science that by neglecting it we are in danger of losing something fundamental. One key point is to get people in the primary schools who are capable of teaching mathematics and a second is to take action about the qualifications of girls entering upon training college courses; a third is to see that at least one lecturer is appointed to each training college staff who is qualified in mathematics. If anyone concerned about good science teaching wants a shock, let him look at the qualifications in mathematics of those who teach and lecture in many of our women's training colleges.

I should like now to refer briefly to the situation in the modern schools. I recently heard a review of timetables of over 1,500 modern schools, which stated how much time was allotted to different subjects. On an average, not more than $1\frac{1}{2}$ hours a week was being given to science. For reasons with which you are all familiar, the staffing problems in most of these schools have for years been almost insurmountable. Despite that fact, one of the most interesting recent developments has been the increasing number of their boys and girls who have taken science at 'O' level in the General Certificate of Education. This tells of much good work, of co-operation between neighbouring schools, and sometimes of co-operation between schools and technical colleges. For selected groups of older pupils the colleges can offer facilities, perhaps on one day a week, to supplement the science facilities in nearby schools.

The modern schools, as well as the longer-established secondary schools, have problems not only of staff but also of equipment; and in times when prices change as rapidly as they have been changing, it is constantly necessary to review allowances for books, stationery, apparatus and equipment. We have to face the fact that if we are to teach a lot more science, it will cost the schools a lot more money for materials. These amounts are not usually separated from those for other subjects. There are authorities which give separate allowances for science, but most of us prefer to trust head masters of schools to allocate between the subjects because the need of one subject in a particular year may be very much greater than in another year. It is, however, most important that we should realize that the books, equipment and furniture for the older pupils are very much more expensive than those for younger pupils. The textbook is no substitute for the teacher, but in these days when there is a shortage of teachers there is a good case for being more generous about textbooks.

I should also like to say a word about visual aids and the National Committee for Visual Aids, an organization supported by local education authorities and also by the British Association and the Ministry of Education. It has produced some attractive films, particularly for advanced science, which I do not think are being used as much as they might be. There is still occasionally some reluctance to take the projector into the science room, a reluctance which should be overcome, for an unused projector is a waste of money which could have been spent on other things. Some of the films which are being produced are very useful teaching aids indeed, and if more schools used them we should get more of them.

A word of praise is due to all those people who have planned, designed and equipped all our new laboratories since the war. The Ministry of Education *Building Bulletins* have been of great value, and the larger authorities now have staffs who have plenty of experience in the kind of problem which has to be solved. No one can be expert in everything, but these advisers know the important points and they know also where to find what is wanted and where to go to get advice—from the Ministry, from teachers and their associations, and from industrial people and specialist firms. They have done very well and we have reason to be proud of many of the laboratories which have been built since the war. No doubt mistakes have been made; for example, many new technical schools have been given too few laboratories. So have some of the girls' schools. The recommendation of the Ministry that girls' schools should have fewer laboratories than boys' schools should be withdrawn. The sizes of some advanced laboratories have been too small. The larger sixth forms which are now normal will overcrowd these laboratories and teaching power will be uneconomically used in them. Nevertheless, I think that the aggregate of L.E.A. achievement for science building in the years 1945-57 and mainly in the second half of that period, is remarkable. I recently had the assistance of many of my colleagues who made a return from all the schools in their areas, both in counties and county boroughs. It was not a country-wide return but it was a very large sample, and it suggests that many more than 4,000 new laboratories have been provided by local education authorities since the war and that over one-third of them have been in grammar and technical schools—a very large share for these selective schools. There are still very many to be built but, given the financial resources, L.E.A.s can certainly face the building problems which remain both in selective schools and in the modern schools.

Dr Hill has reminded us that local education authorities provide technical education as well as primary and secondary education. Anyone who looks at the history of English education since 1900 will see that a division grew up, perhaps unnecessarily, between secondary and technical education and it was not until after the last war that proper efforts were made to break it down. It is being broken down in many areas. The former junior technical schools have become recognized secondary schools, and the grammar schools are doing many things which used to be regarded as technical. While there is still some evidence of a cleavage between technical education and secondary education, yet in the next few years there is a good chance to bring about a much better relationship. The local authorities are investing substantial resources in new technical colleges which are worthy of some of the best students who cannot enter universities. Our vocational guidance staffs are well aware of the possibilities at such colleges and I hope they will get many more part-time, ' sandwich ' and full-time students from all kinds of secondary school and that in consequence many more boys will find careers in applied science.

SESSION IV

GENERAL DISCUSSION

Sir Raymond Priestley, Chairman

THE CHAIRMAN. We have agreed that this afternoon the first hour shall be devoted to general discussion on any topic that any member of the audience wishes to raise, after which I shall ask Lord Tedder to summarize our two days' work. But before throwing open the meeting to you all, I should like to ask Sir Gilbert Flemming, who has been referred to on several occasions during our debates and has sat through them with admirable patience and imperturbability, to do a little answering back.

SIR GILBERT FLEMMING (*Permanent Secretary to the Ministry of Education*). I have no intention at all of answering back, but there are one or two things that I should like to say. First, I want to express the thanks of my Minister and Ministry to the British Association for organizing this Conference, and my personal thanks for the opportunity of hearing both the set speakers and the others. I may have seemed imperturbable, but I have been exceedingly interested. My chief job here is to be seen, and not heard, so that you may know that I am ready to act as a messenger of what I have heard. The fact that I do not comment on many of the points that have been raised does not mean that I have not been noting them.

Several comments that I might have made have been made for me by other people. I should like, as my contribution to the discussion of the teacher problem, to bring together and to put in proper proportion a number of facts that have been mentioned by other speakers but not, as it seems to me, in quite the right relation to each other.

I do not think that anyone has brought out quite clearly why we have had two quite different theme songs running through our discussions, the first, the intense difficulty—described by Dr Barton—

125

of conditions in the schools since the war as compared with those before the war; and the other, the success story—the results achieved in the schools as shown by the great increase in the number of 'A' level passes, the flow to the universities and so on.

Why were conditions apparently so easy in the schools before the war? For what, to me, is the perfectly scandalous reason that the nation was not then prepared to do a serious educational job at all— I think that twenty years is long enough after the event for me, as a civil servant, to describe a position as scandalous. In 1938 only about 2 per cent of the 17-year age group was continuing its education in maintained schools, and, if you take in the direct-grant and independent schools as well, about 5 per cent of the population was being educated to the age of 17 plus. Now, thank goodness, in the maintained schools it has risen from 2 per cent to 6 per cent, and in all schools it is about 10 per cent. I do not give ourselves as a nation any great bouquets for working it up to 10 per cent, but this increase by itself, quite apart from the increased demand for science graduates from other employers, makes it not at all surprising that the schools are finding it far more difficult to get enough good teachers of science.

I do not quote my improved percentages as an excuse for not making the greatest possible effort. I mention them only as showing that, in the absolute sense, we are making immense progress, and it is, therefore, profoundly worth while giving that extra shove, the case for which we have heard so strongly pressed during the Conference. It is not a question of reversing an existing trend and suddenly going in a new direction but of helping the right trend with a far more vigorous push. That is the picture for the country as a whole, though I can well imagine that that is not how it looks if one is working under great difficulties in some particular school.

To put it in simple numerical terms, some people talk as if the number of graduate teachers of science in the schools was actually getting smaller. On the contrary, there has been a big increase, but not big enough. I did not quite follow Dr Barton's reasoning which led to the deficiency being estimated at a thousand. As he knows the subject so intimately I expect that his figure is related to some definite standard; but when I heard the figure mentioned I said to myself, 'If it is only a thousand, we can do that all right—but I think we need more.' The number of pupils in the sixth forms is growing rapidly, and the consequent output from the universities will also grow so that we can reasonably expect a bigger rate of increase than we have been getting. To make good a deficiency of a thousand teachers of science would not therefore worry me as unduly difficult.

But, in relation to any proper demand, can we hope to see the supply becoming adequate? I do not think so—and, provocatively, I do not hope so. For the same sort of reason as makes me regard the pre-war position as scandalous, I would, in the near future, regard any situation as scandalous in which it seemed to be easy to get enough science teachers.

As I see it, this could only be because we were not putting our demands high enough. But you scientists are quite rightly all the time stimulating new demands. I am not at all satisfied, for instance, with the 10 per cent who are now enjoying the full grammar school curriculum. Sir Solly said, quite rightly, that present trends might bring us in not many years to 15 per cent. I do not know what you think of 15 per cent. Plenty of people would like to go even further. And these percentages relate to pupils in all kinds of school studying all kinds of subject. If within the totals we also hope that more attention will be paid to science teaching, then I cannot see the supply of science teachers becoming easy in any foreseeable time. Nor should it be, because we should all look ahead to the next job that needs to be done.

That is no reason for not putting all one can into the present drive. It only takes me to the practical conclusion that for an indefinite period, and for right and worthy reasons for which we do not need to apologize, qualified science teachers should be thought of, and treated, as rare jewels of great price. All the devices and dodges for treating them as such, which may seem wrong to those who remember pre-war days, should not be apologized for or thought of as something that will pass, but should be accepted as something right and proper of which one ought to be proud just as one is proud of treating a rare jewel carefully.

As a corollary to that, those of us not actually in the front line have an added responsibility for seeing that science teachers have the best possible opportunities and conditions so that their skill and time and effort are not wasted. I am thinking now of the remarks that have been made about equipment, technicians and so on. But

127

also as a corollary—and I am glad that this was said by Miss Huxstep in her remarks about time-and-motion study—it is our duty to see that this scarce man- and womanpower is used as efficiently as possible.

It is also our job, collectively, to look out for any exceptional windfalls that may come or be produced by a judicious shaking of the tree. There is, for example, the possibility of more men being drawn from the Services. At the Ministry, we have taken a great deal of trouble to keep in touch with those men, and it is on experience of the actual men coming forward that our plans for encouraging some of them to take training college courses are based. Sir Graham Savage wants us to take more sensational action. We will keep our eyes open for this possibility, but on our actual experience I think that our apparently humdrum proposals are right.

I want now, rather daringly, to try to put some of the remarks made about girls and women in slightly different perspective, although all the points I shall make have already been made. Comparison with pre-war conditions is, for the reasons already pointed out, doubly misleading. There was no shortage of women teachers between the wars, for two reasons. The massacre of men in the first world war had deprived many women of their husbands; and the industrial and social conditions afterwards made it hard for people to marry and bring up families. For purely personal reasons, I agree warmly with Dame Kathleen that it was a wicked waste for the women science graduates of those years to have been deprived of an opportunity of becoming mothers. I hope that the conditions which applied between the wars will never come again.

Therefore, for the girls' schools even more than for the schools as a whole, the need for looking to expedients and dodges, for employing part-timers, for getting women back into teaching after they have brought up their families and so on, has to be accepted as something permanent, and accepted with pride and enthusiasm, and not grudgingly as though it were a grievance. I welcomed what I heard about refresher courses for married women who are thinking of returning to teaching. At the Ministry, we have been watching that venture with interest. If it develops in any way that calls for national action, I hope that we shall be ready to help. But it seems to me more likely to call for local action, and I am grateful to those who have acted locally without waiting for the Ministry.

I have been a little disappointed that the tone of the discussion has not quite faced the realities, as I see them, of women's lives and careers as they are now. I very much agree with Dame Kathleen that the mere exhortation of women to take up scientific and technical careers is silly and a waste of time and paper; but it also seems a waste of time to talk of the valuable reservoir of skilled womanpower, unless you go on to face the facts of modern social life and present social trends and habits.

Of course, you may think that we should be guided by Russia, where every woman automatically continues her career after marriage whether it is in the factory, the laboratory or the hospital ward, taking a few months off for childbearing and leaving the children for grandmother to look after. I cannot see our society moving very rapidly in that direction, and as far as I can see, only the extremely able, enthusiastic, devoted and lucky women will be able to continue their careers during the time of child-bearing and supervision of the young family. We have to realize that the normal prospects of women are, as Miss Huxstep sketched out, a few years of employment, a period with the family, and then—we hope—a return, either to part-time or possibly to full-time employment.

I draw two conclusions from that. Those who emphasize the importance of drawing womanpower into our skilled services, whether teaching or anything else, should see that the career can fit into that pattern. If you cannot do that, do not pretend that you can—because it never gets you anywhere. Our record in teaching is not too bad. I hope that we can do even better by going further in the acceptance of part-time work and the return to teaching of the older married women.

I draw the other conclusion that, with the age of marriage and childbearing getting lower and lower, as it does every year, it is futile and dishonest to pretend that the training and educating of more women makes for a large, immediate increase in effective working power. That is not a reason for not doing it. We need to improve the education of women on broad educational grounds. I am a believer in that from the long-term view, but, we shall

129

not be honest if we pretend that it will provide a short cut to the supply of urgently needed womanpower.

I feel rash speaking as a man like this, but I have been a little depressed when talking to women who have got just to the edge of facing the social facts which lead to this conclusion and then have shied back. Perhaps I can be acquitted of having any bias against women in this matter, if I conclude by mentioning my personal reason for supporting Dame Kathleen so strongly in commending the science graduate as a wife and a mother. It is not that I am married to one, but that I had the even greater privilege of having one for my mother—which was rare when I was born. She was a science graduate teacher in a school of some standing 70 years ago. That is why I do not like the pre-war pattern, but it is also why I say that we must remember the conditions of the world as it is today.

I cannot see us going Russian. I prefer to rest the case for girls' education, scientific or otherwise, on broad arguments that hold water, and not on arguments which may be related to our short-term requirements, but which do not seem to me to face the realities of the social situation in this country.

Most of the facts to which I have drawn attention have been mentioned by others, and all I have done has been to put a few of them in context one with another. In any case my chief job here is not to be listened to, but to be visibly here.

MRS E. W. PARSONS (*Chairman, Cambridgeshire Education Committee*). May I allay any suspicion that may be aroused by the announcement that I am Chairman of the Cambridgeshire Education Committee by saying that I was first a scientist, and I hope I still am and shall remain a scientist. I am also a grandmother of many, so perhaps this may be accounted grandmother's day. Perhaps, too, I may be thought to have made a personal contribution to the supply of scientists; how great, the next 20 years will show. Meanwhile, I cannot help remembering that at least one of the F_1 generation said: 'I know all about science, and I suppose I have to be educated, although what I really want to do is to get married and have twelve children.' At the same time, I hope that I have done something to alleviate this shortage of which I myself am so conscious.

Throughout my life I have been concerned with the eighteen-year-old student and selection for universities. The difficulty of entrance for the girl who goes round from one university to another to the number of half a dozen, has caused much concern. That has been mentioned both yesterday and today, so that when I heard Dame Kathleen's suggestion for earlier entry into the universities and a less exacting standard, I wondered whether that would, in fact, do anything to help, particularly with regard to scientists. I am not at all sure that it would.

My own view is that 18 is generally quite young enough for the scientist to go to the university, but there is something to be said for getting the best ones on in the maintained schools better than we are doing at present. I often wonder whether we could not deal with the quicker ones as the non-maintained schools—the preparatory and public schools—do. If we were to try we should meet with difficulties arising from staffing and time-tabling —and I am old-fashioned enough to hope that we shall never crowd Latin out of the curriculum altogether. But I do hope that the time may come when we may get away from too slavish adherence to age limits. The examining bodies were at one time bound by age conditions, but they are now freer, so that the really good 17-year-old should be able to avoid a year's delay.

Reverting to the question of selection for entrance to universities, I should like to tell you what we have tried in Cambridge in founding our new little college—New Hall—which we hope will grow bigger in time. We have abandoned the more rigid method of examination of students in favour of using the school estimate, an essay paper and a series of interviews. Although we have been going only three years—which is not long enough—we have reason to believe that we may be able to reduce the tremendous pressure caused by competitive entrance. Of course, we have not yet affected the pressure, because we are admitting only 15 a year, and every girl who tries for New Hall is also trying for half a dozen or so other places. But we hope to show that there may be a new method of selection that is less exacting and trying than the old.

I should like to mention another point which has not, I think, been touched upon, namely, the possibility of change from one academic discipline to another—from other disciplines to the reading of science—and to remind you of that very far-sighted

131

and interesting venture, the I.C.I. bursary scheme. I have seen a good deal of the working of that scheme in Cambridge, and it is interesting to observe that men who started reading for another Tripos have, with encouragement, very successfully changed to science.

My next point is concerned with Dr Chesterman's four-year course, either the ' 3 plus 1 '—the degree course plus a training year—or the three-year teacher training course plus one academic year. We have to remember here that although we may get many teachers out of them we cannot make ultimate teaching a condition of entry to those courses. I do not think, however, that we should lose many, and there should be a hopeful future for that scheme. But we must be careful not to coerce the 17- or 18-year-olds into deciding on their future careers too soon. I have seen a little of that kind of thing on my committee for making awards—major awards—to boys and girls going to the university. My heart always sinks when my colleagues invite boys and girls appearing before us to say what they hope to do after graduation. I know quite well what the answer will be—they are all going to do research, or, perhaps, research into research!

It is a mistake to press young people to make up their minds at that stage, unless, indeed, they happen to have their minds made up for other reasons. If they have made them up, and are going to training colleges, well and good, and the science supplementary courses can afford a very encouraging continuation. Those supplementary courses, so far as I have seen them at work in Cambridge and elsewhere, have, indeed, been of the greatest possible help to the secondary modern schools. But we must go on thinking about the supplementary courses, because the content of them may need to change quite a good deal in the future. Perhaps, also, the teachers who have taken them may need yet further help; the provision of further help for those non-graduate science teachers in our schools is worthy of serious consideration.

MR F. L. ALLAN. I want to refer to what Dame Kathleen Lonsdale said this morning about the proper age for going to university. It may be good for girls to leave school at 17—I do not know. But for boys the final third year in the sixth form is invaluable, not only for academic education—important though that is, it could take place in a preliminary year at university—but because the boy is helped to grow up by accepting responsibility and facing difficulties. In that year in the sixth form he is the important boy at the top of the school, whereas, at the university, he would be a 'fresher' and unimportant. Education consists not only of acquiring academic knowledge but, in the case of boys, of producing effective and useful men of the world. I venture to question whether the age of 17 is appropriate for transfer from grammar school to university.

There is another point, on which I do wholeheartedly agree with Dame Kathleen—indeed, with the one exception I have just mentioned I agree with all that she said. I refer to her point about the need for greater energy and enterprise in encouraging recruitment of teachers. *The Times* recently had three supplements on careers, but in the papers it printed there was nothing at all about teaching. If there is another supplement of that kind we must try to persuade *The Times* to remember that teaching is an important career.

Again, the *Manchester Guardian* is at present carrying a series of full-page advertisements—at £500 a page—by the great industrialists, pointing out the importance and the promise of the careers which they offer. But there is nothing of this kind to publicize the advantages of the teaching profession. I wonder whether the Ministry of Education, who are primarily concerned, could not spend £500 on publicity of that sort?

Dame Kathleen also spoke about the possibility of visits to universities by science masters and others to give third-year undergraduates the facts about teaching—its attractions and importance.

Some exploratory steps have already been taken. Sir Eric James has been to Oxford and, by courtesy of the Appointments Board, I recently went to Birmingham. I was delighted to find myself in a lecture room filled by about a hundred young men and women who thought it worth while to listen to an hour's talk about prospects in the teaching profession. They were certainly alert; they asked the right questions and I discovered afterwards, in the Careers Committee of the Head Masters' Association of which I am Chairman, that my talk had had actual practical effects. Two head masters told me that they had been able to recruit to their science staffs men who had been influenced by what I had said.

Dame Kathleen told us that the Committee of Vice-Chancellors and Principals is to consider with heads of schools, whether such co-operation shall become a routine matter in the future. I hope that it will be so, but the arts of persuasion brought to bear on the young must not be routine. It is important that the right things should be said with vitality and in a convincing manner. I am certain that the right type of science masters could be found, who would be ready to accept the invitation of the universities to visit them and state the case for teaching as a profession.

A good deal too much has been said about the discrepancy between the salaries of school masters and mistresses and what they would get in a comparable position in industry or elsewhere. In the early stages, at any rate, a school master joining a school will earn only £50 or £100 less than he would in industry. It is true that if you remain in industry and go to the top of the tree there are most desirable plums, but not everybody gets to the top of the tree—and salary, after all, is not the only consideration. At least, it can be said that the school master has the prospect of a reasonable financial competence. Two-thirds of my colleagues in a typical grammar school of large to moderate size, receive more than £1,000 a year. The school master will never be a wealthy man, but it is mistaken to think that he will be impoverished.

MR A. E. MILLETT (*Vice-Chairman, Education Committee, Kesteven, Lincs*). I represent the local authority point of view and the first thing I want to impress on the Conference is the fact that educational standards and progress depend on the availability of money. I am cross with Alderman Hill, who has shown no comprehension of this new scheme of grants for education and other things. When the preliminary five years have passed either the rates of the local authorities will go up substantially, or the educational standards will go down.

Let us imagine for a minute what is to happen next year, when we know what we are going to get—and we do not yet know just what we shall get even for next year. Whatever the amount, the finance committee of a county council will meet to decide how to apportion it between the various services of the county. In some county councils, the highways committee is a very great force in the finance committee, and the education committee comes next. In my county I am glad to say that the education committee comes first, or I just do not know what would happen.

In 1947, Kesteven was one of the authorities with the lowest possible standard of education in the country; today it stands as one of the best, and has one of the highest education rates. And what do we get for that? We get from the Ministry of Education something that it calls a quota of teachers for the county—a figure based on some fantastic formula under which the Ministry informs us that as a county we are 31 teachers above our quota. That is our reward for trying to raise the standard of education in Kesteven. The result is that where there were 19 in the average grammar school class we will have to put it up to 20; the numbers in the average class in the secondary modern school will go up from 24 to 26. That is not progress in education.

The obstructions that we have met with from the Ministry of Education are almost unbelievable. They came out a year or two ago with the slogan that rural reorganization was vital to the interests of the country. Eighteen months later they changed their minds and refused to let us build a new secondary modern school. We still have scores of all-age schools, and until we have reorganized them we cannot make any progress. Six months ago we decided that every secondary modern school should have a rural science unit, costing about £4,000. We had to fight tooth and nail with the Ministry for consent for those units, even for the new schools we have built. Then they turn and say, ' Your other four rural secondary schools must be postponed for twelve months.'

Since 1947, my authority has taken over a training college for 120 men and women students. We have established a farm institute and—and this is very important—we have developed a technical college which now has a total student population of some 6,000. But we get no encouragement to go forward, and what will happen with the block grant, I do not know.

Let me quote one instance to show what the county education authority is up against. Next year, our rates are to be 2s. 6d. in the £ more than they were last year—justifiably, because we made a mistake last year. Most of that increase is for education. On our border we have a minor borough of 11,000 population, and the borough council decided to ask another county to take them in because we had put up the rates by 2s. 6d. They quite forgot to look at the record of the other county where the rates, for more than ten years had been 2s. more than those at Kesteven.

Finally, I will refer to something said by Dame Kathleen. She spoke of shortening the period in the sixth form in grammar schools. I should want to be given very cogent reasons for taking such a decision. I am governor of two public schools and several grammar schools, and in my opinion the last two years in a grammar school sixth form, at 16 to 18 or 17 to 19 years of age, are the most vital in the life of a boy or girl. During those two years, not only does their outlook on life become different, but they become more stable and balanced, so that when they go to the university they are worthy of their place there. I would hate to see that period shortened.

MR G. L. WATT (*Head of Science Department, Holloway School*). I was rather on the side of what Dame Kathleen Lonsdale said about sixth forms. But what can we do? The principal reason for keeping people for a third year is that, otherwise, we cannot get them to the standard now required for entrance to universities.

In providing further academic training for teachers who have been to training colleges, it is unreasonable to suggest that those who have done a proper day's work in a science laboratory at school should have to go to evening classes, at least during their first two years of teaching. If they are doing their work properly during the week, they will be too tired by Friday night to do anything of the sort.

I think that we have been looking at our problems today in too narrow a context. It is not sufficient, either here or elsewhere, to concern ourselves only with science teachers and science accommodation. We have to consider the basic problem, that is the problem of overcrowding at all levels, and particularly in the primary school. I do not know whether my colleagues have found the same thing, but I often find pupils in their first year who can understand the science and the experiments but cannot write them up and cannot do the calculations. So it is absolutely essential that we should tackle first things first. Let us begin with smaller classes in the primary schools, and then we can deal with the secondary schools.

On the front page of the current *Times Educational Supplement* there is a notice of a new pamphlet on teacher supply from which anyone can see just how critical the classroom situation will be in the next few years. Apparently in the sixties there will not be an end of the ' bulge ' but a continuation of it. No matter what we decide now about more laboratories and equipment, the whole question of teacher and classroom supply will be increasingly urgent, and we cannot possibly put that right on 3 per cent of the national income. We shall not get more teachers or more classroom accommodation with the block grant for local education authorities. Nobody in the education world believes that we shall; and these basic financial problems will have to be solved before children in the primary and secondary schools can be taught in classes of reasonable size. Then we may be able to give them interesting practical work in the first two years at the secondary schools. If we can get so far, we shall not have any difficulty in the future about the supply of science teachers.

MISS EASTWOOD (*Godolphin and Latymer School, W*.6). When Miss Huxstep said that 25 per cent of the time in girls' grammar schools was devoted to mathematics and science she did not go on to say that about half of that time was spent on mathematics. I think it is time that the claims of that subject were re-examined.

In the primary schools and the grammar schools children do arithmetic or mathematics every day from the age of six for about ten years. Then if they wish to take science they may be faced with a very difficult decision. They may not wish to give up hope of reading mathematics at the university and so they are told that they must take both pure and applied mathematics at 'A' level. If they want to keep the alternative of doing science they must also take 'A' level physics and chemistry. This is too great a load. Is it really necessary to take both pure and applied mathematics? If the syllabus could be reduced, our pupils would have time for both science and some outside subjects and the number of pure mathematicians would not be greatly reduced.

The Science Masters' Association and the Association of Women Science Teachers can always give a lead on the claims of the various sciences for curriculum time. The chemists, physicists and biologists there have to justify themselves to each other. The mathematicians do not have to account for themselves so strictly. It seems that the universities themselves should perhaps begin by considering their entrance requirements.

I was very glad that Dr Chesterman did not recommend the formal study of science in primary schools. Of course, one should attempt to answer children's questions, but there is a real danger if systematic physical science is attempted at too early a stage.

I should like also to ask for an examination of research and research grants. I am sure there is pruning to be done there, and that much of the time now spent on routine research might be devoted to consideration of teaching problems, to devising experiments, for instance, which would make new branches of the subject understandable and attractive to the young.

I support Dr Barton on the subject of local authorities. It is difficult to believe that keeping down expenditure on equipment is always justified by the administrative cost of doing so. You may be in the middle of a difficult exposition to the sixth form and be called away by a message saying that you are required urgently on the telephone. When you get there you find a clerk, who asks: ' Why do you want to buy so-and-so? ' Perhaps this is where accountancy is running ahead of teaching. Authorities are often generous, but one sometimes feels that it is a generous tyranny.

DAME KATHLEEN LONSDALE: I expected to be shot at on the question of the school-leaving age, but I would point out that if the school-leaving age is brought back to 17, your head boy gets his experience of responsibility at that age instead of at 18. He gets a little more responsibility at a little earlier age. I was head girl at 15, went to the university at 16, and cannot believe that it is absolutely necessary to defer responsibility to 18 or 19 years of age. I plead only for a reconsideration of the present trend, with perhaps a little more flexibility.

SUMMING UP

THE RT. HON. THE LORD TEDDER, G.C.B.

THE CHAIRMAN. We all know Lord Tedder as a great war leader, and now that you see us standing here side by side you will also realize that he has the secret of eternal youth. He went to Cambridge as an undergraduate four years before me, and took his degree, as you will not be surprised to learn, nine years before I did. We both served in the first world war. He performed signal service in the R.F.C.—I performed in the Signal Service. I now owe him allegiance as Chancellor of my University.

LORD TEDDER. I have listened to this Conference with very great interest. In the face of such a volume of expert knowledge and experience it would be foolish for me to attempt to sum up —all I can do is to offer the comments that occur to me as a layman.

In the first place I would say that nearly everything I have heard here has completely confirmed an opinion I have had for years, which is that science is no longer an exclusive black art. It is not merely an integral part of modern life, but an essential part of the modern culture. If, in some respects, it is not yet fully accepted in that place, it is your task to establish it there.

The second thing that struck me was the reference to the gulf between—I will not say the humanities because that gives the immediate implication that science is inhuman—but between science and the arts. That, in itself, is a bad differentiation, because, after all, there is much art in scientific work. I have seen people doing research, and if much of it is not art I do not know what is. That gulf, if it exists—and for once I agree with Sir Eric James—must be filled up; and if there is a wall it must be pulled down.

The references made this morning to the six-year-olds were very important. I have been heckled by small boys two or three years older than six about the difference between fission and fusion. When I turned the question on to them, they gave me quite a reasonable definition; they just wanted to see whether I knew! I do not suggest that there is need for systematic scientific training in the elementary schools, but there must be some way of letting these children know—someone whom they can question. They have a right to know and the sooner they get intelligent and intelligible explanations the better; the less likely they are to go off the rails. So if we are to have an informed public opinion we must start at the bottom. We do not want scare headlines, nor the other extreme, the soporific brush-off. We do want a balanced understanding about the facts of modern life.

In that connection, I would ask you scientists to try to simplify your language. It is sometimes very difficult for us laymen to understand what you are talking about and we are, therefore, disposed to wonder whether you always understand yourselves. I have asked a number of scientists to try to help on this, and once or twice I have come across what I think is a very dangerous reaction, ' Oh, well, it is very complicated. Now, so-and-so has written some articles on it; popular stuff—not really accurate or scientific—it is most undesirable.' I ask you not to be intellectual snobs. If these things cannot be explained by you who know what you are talking about, the road is left open to the charlatans, and charlatans are dangerous.

I cannot go through the whole series of discussions—about the schools (primary, secondary modern, grammar, and the rest) and about technical colleges and universities—but I do think that the printed record of these proceedings will be well worth study. I shall read it with great care myself, and I know that I shall learn a great deal more than I know now. Today I can pick out one or two general points that have impressed me, as an individual.

First, there is that new law—the James law. I do not see Sir Eric here, but I hope that he will not mind my suggesting that, perhaps, his new law, his conservation of curricula, is merely a new version of the old saying about cutting one's coat. What I should have liked to hear more about is how he applies that law in relation to the specialization in his own sixth form. I have a complex about over-specialization. I have felt sometimes that there is a conflict between specialization on the one side and education, in the real sense of the word, on the other. Perhaps I am wrong, or prejudiced, but I should like to have heard Sir Eric on the subject.

I feel that I must express my views on something which was said by Dame Kathleen Lonsdale. I do most strongly disagree with the idea of sending boys to university at 17 years of age and so cutting off a year at school. In a boy's development, that last year at school is a most—the most—important one. Of course, there are exceptions, but the chances are nine to one that if a boy goes to university at 17 he will be too young to get full benefit from it.

That leads me to another point about sixth form education. I suggest that a boy who gets in his full time in the sixth form with creditable performance has really achieved something well worth having in itself. I believe that in many cases that may be an adequate and satisfactory educational target for a boy or girl. At present, there seems to be an idea that every such boy or girl *must* go on to a university. But the universities are already over-crowded and will get more so, and a lot of boys who do well up to the sixth form would do better to get out into the world rather than go on to the academic life.

Sir Gilbert Flemming has dealt with many of the points with which I felt that I should deal, and I was relieved to hear him say in relation to the supply of teachers that nobody was thinking, at present, of adopting the Russian policy and directing people into teaching and other professions. That might be a simple solution, but one does not feel that it is quite a British way, and it is good to know that it is not at present contemplated. On the other hand there is much to be said for asking universities to give a more definite lead towards the teaching profession.

The word 'economy' has been mentioned several times. There is one form of economy that is not dangerous—in fact it is essential —and that is the economy which consists of making the best possible use of what we have. Sir Gilbert made sympathetic noises in reply to Sir Graham Savage but he used the word 'humdrum' to describe the Ministry's approach to the recruitment of ex-officers; this is an immediate problem, and I do not like 'humdrum.'

As an outsider listening to all this discussion, my general impression is that the problem has been exhaustively dealt with and admirably analysed. We can now see the excellent way in which the Ministry and the local authorities have done the best they could in limiting circumstances, and have always shown vision and drive. One of the things that does really thrill one is to hear of the wonderful improvisations and of the loyalty with which people have met immediate difficulties that cannot be solved by conventional means. It is all rather inspiring.

If ever there was an Oliver Twist, it is education. You will never be satisfied, as I think Sir Gilbert feels, because, although Sir Solly Zuckerman gave comforting estimates as to the future—and I would have the greatest hesitation in doubting his analysis—it does not follow that we shall get what he says we ought to have.

Of one thing I am quite sure, and that is that there will be demands for more money, particularly and justifiably for secondary modern school laboratories and equipment. The Industrial Fund has shown what can be done quickly if there is a determined attack. Incidentally, I notice one other good thing about industrialists—they have, apparently, a very healthy disregard for examination results. I am rather pleased at this symptom of real culture.

That is all that I have to say. I think you have had a valuable Conference. I hope that it will have the effects wished for, which are first to educate the public, and then to explain to people in the teaching profession how their various problems are related. It is always difficult in one place to realize that your own immediate difficulties are closely related with those of people in other places and with national problems which affect us all.

THE CHAIRMAN. I know that you will wish me to thank Lord Tedder. He spoke of one thing that has been concerning the British Association for some time, namely, the obscure language of science. I have personal feelings about this. I once read a paper called 'Aspects of Polar Exploration,' but I always suspected that it was not good science because it was the only article in the journal that I could understand!

In the last two days, a notable gathering, half a thousand strong, has attempted a re-assessment of a vital problem. One thing that seems to me to stand out a mile is that the first requirement for its solution is a very considerable increase in national expenditure on education. And that is not going to be easy to find. Comparisons with such countries as Sweden or Switzerland are unrealistic. They have neither our defence commitments nor our moral obligation to assist in the development of half a dozen countries and dependent peoples.

I think the time has come when Britain must face up to two main facts. First, if we are adequately to man the key sections of our economy without direction of labour—up with which, to use a Churchillism, we will not put—we can only do so by adequate incentives, no matter how strongly many of us may feel about the desirability of matching equality of opportunity with equality of reward.

Second, we must remember the size of the cake, which has been referred to this morning. Dame Kathleen suggested that in a less crazy world the large sums required would be found by cutting the defence vote and military research. I agree—in a less crazy world. In the meantime, accepting the facts of life, may I suggest an alternative that would touch our individual pockets more closely. It is arguable that the time is rapidly approaching—if if has not already arrived—when it will be worth while to call a halt in the accumulation of luxurious amenities, and even comforts, in so far as their purchase involves absorbing the proceeds of increasing productive capacity, and to invest the money in the education of our youth as an insurance against lack of the necessities of life in the next stage of development of what is still a competitive world.

Turning to the present Conference, I suggest that the best way of getting the utmost from it would be for the British Association to ask its organizing committee to consider the whole record, when it has been compiled; to write a carefully considered postscript to the book, and then to consider what action should be taken—perhaps with special reference to the remarks of Dr Barton yesterday. I am not in favour of *ad hoc* resolutions, which often, I think, do more harm than good.

May I, now, on behalf of the British Association, thank the President and Council of the Royal Geographical Society for their hospitality. Then we must thank all those responsible for the extraordinary efforts that have been made for our comfort and for the smooth running of our meeting. Lastly, may I ask Mr

Poskitt, of Bolton School, to come on to the platform. I understand that he wishes to make a proposition that touches the British Association and, therefore, myself, more closely.

Mr F. R. Poskitt (*Head Master, Bolton School*): It is my very great pleasure to express, on behalf of all attending, our very great thanks to the British Association for the work it has done in making this Conference possible, and particularly to Sir Raymond Priestley, to Sir George Allen, the General Secretary and to his secretary, Miss Lowry-Corry, who has carried out so much of the detailed work; and to all who, as speakers on the platform or as contributors from the floor, have taken part in our discussions. I think it is very likely that the immediate object of our Conference will be achieved. But there is a danger that those of us who have attended will then sit back and think we have done our part. If that happens we shall miss one of the most important results that should come from this Conference—something which Lord Tedder felt was rather important.

It will be all very good if we do get the laboratories and the teachers, but there still remains the major question, the one raised by Sir Eric James—namely what we do when we have them. Those of us who are teachers will then have to deal with possibly the most critical issue our profession has faced for four or five hundred years. It is not really a question of raising our material standards of living, of securing the welfare of the community, or its defence, or anything like that. We have to integrate into our cultural tradition the whole body of new scientific and other knowledge gained in the last fifty years. That will not be done merely by having more laboratories and more teachers—even teachers of quality.

This is not the time to go into all the problems involved, such as curricula for the general education of scientists and the scientific education of the arts man; but there is one thing that we teachers should take away from this meeting. It is the thought that whereas we can do very little in some of the spheres that have been discussed, we can do a great deal in our own minds to prepare ourselves and our colleagues for what must be a great revolution in the structure of our curricula and our whole approach to education. I sometimes suspect that the greatest obstacle in

144

the way of integration of our culture and getting rid of the barriers, which are probably entirely false, between humanism—or the arts—and science, is the attitude of some of us in our own schools. The controversy about the balanced curriculum may well appear as ludicrous in the future as the arid arguments of the schoolmen.

We all do feel a great sense of gratitude to the British Association, and if this Conference proves fruitful, our responsibility is to see that, beyond more and better science teaching methods, its influence will reach into the realms of education in a very much wider and deeper way. Our problems are not only the concern of university examining bodies and the like. We shall have to settle many of them in our own ranks.

It is possibly with the thought of battles yet to come, in which we may need the assistance of the British Association in thinking out our problems, that I am able to offer thanks, on behalf of everyone present, for the favours we have received.

POSTSCRIPT

by

W. H. PERKINS, O.B.E.
Formerly County Education Officer for Warwickshire

Lord Tedder has summed up, and Sir Raymond Priestley, in prescribing a carefully considered postscript, has pointed very clearly to the central factor which must govern any further actions about the subject of our Conference.

The 'either—or' situation has been made clear enough. For all the values by which we live, moral, aesthetic, or intellectual, we must accept technology, if not all its works. Otherwise hunger, disease, and the austerities of nature will drive a growing world population backward towards barbarism rather than forward to brotherhood. If we in this island are to remain prosperous ourselves and generous to the less fortunate, we need a much bolder programme of rapid educational advance than any which has yet been promulgated. The Conference, which started to consider science in schools, ended with a requirement (which, in Sir Raymond Priestley's words 'stands out a mile') of far more money for public education. The development of science and technology cannot take place without better provision for every legitimate activity of schools, colleges and universities.

The provision must come from public funds—from rates and taxes—and the planning for it therefore has political aspects which are apt to make the educationist and the scientist rather impatient. It is possible that an inquiry by a non-political, unofficial body—including educators, economists, sociologists and industrialists—might put the problem in its right proportions and confront the public with clear issues. Let us try to define some of the issues provisionally to see, if we can, how inquiry should develop. We have agreed that we must expand our education system and pay for the expansion from the public purse. So we ask: What are we spending now? How much should we be spending? How quickly should we expand? How should we get the extra money? Who can acceptably explain to the public what is wanted?

It seems that the Ministry of Education, the Scottish Education Department and the local education authorities in Great Britain are proposing to spend rather less than £700 million in 1958-59. To this, for present purposes, it is reasonable to add about £50 million which is distributed to the universities in Treasury grants. The grand total of nearly £750 million admittedly includes some expenditure which should be labelled welfare rather than education (meals, milk, maintenance grants to pupils and students). On the other hand it does not nearly contain a full year's expenditure on new building and capital projects, which are financed by loans repayable over long periods. So, subject to further refinement, we can start from the fact that £750 million is roughly the current rate of public expenditure on education. Out of a gross national product of around £20,000 million this is about 3·75 per cent, appreciably more already than the 3 per cent which is in some minds a national standard not to be exceeded.

The rate of growth of public expenditure in recent years has been rapid—in six years the Ministry of Education's own share has expanded by over 75 per cent (from £214 million to £381 million). There are projects in the early stage of development and other expansion trends which make a total spending of £1,000 million seem likely in the very early 1960's. It is obvious, therefore, that those who want much more and who want it quickly should be thinking in terms of about £1,200 million or even more, plus any additions caused by monetary inflation. This kind of expansion is greater—very much greater—than the growth of the national product, and it is inevitable that if education is to have a larger share in the national economy now, there must be a smaller share for something else. What should the something else be? It is at this point that the voices of economists and industrialists must be heard in our inquiry. Dame Kathleen Lonsdale would save on defence and there will be many to support her. Sir Raymond Priestley foresees restraint in expenditure on consumption goods, and it is difficult to avoid his conclusion, whatever is done about defence.

If an inquiry were to proceed along these lines, and if it were to lead to Sir Raymond's conclusion, then no voice would be too powerful to announce to the British people that they must put learning before luxury until the rise in front of them has been breasted.

The other recurrent call for action in the Conference is much more difficult to handle. Dr Barton and others want an immediate plan which will give the schools a better share of the scientists who are graduating today. They claim, in effect, that we are consuming our seed corn, and that without more science teachers in the schools the crop of ultimate graduates may become smaller and weaker. There appear to be only two solutions. The first would be a quota system of allocation between industry, Government, the schools and the universities. The teaching profession has already had experience of quotas and it does not like them— they do not differ greatly from pure direction of labour. The other solution would be financial—to bring educational salaries for scientists up to industrial salaries. That would inevitably mean a much greater differentiation between the top figures and the basic figures of the Burnham Scales. It might even mean that the science teacher as a result of the 'test of the market', was paid more than others who are not so scarce.

Many people think that the distribution problem will solve itself in due time; but it is more serious than that, and should be discussed soon with a sense of urgency by those who employ scientists, and by those who fix their salaries. The Russian example will be quoted, as it has been by several speakers. It should not be followed, but if it is studied in detail there may be hints towards a British plan.

The Conference on which we are reporting was composed mainly of educationists, that is to say of teachers, education officers, and members of local authorities. Government and industry, to whose notice many of its arguments will have to be brought, were represented, it is true, but not in any great numbers. No educator was impish enough to call for comment on the frequently heard request of industrialists for reductions in Government expenditure. But some discussion of it, with the production of trained manpower as its text, is overdue. If it could take place with an economist in the chair we might hear whether production could be stimulated more by reducing rates and taxes or by increasing them for the specific purpose of providing more highly trained personnel for industry.

The other problem which was clearly stated, but still left largely unsolved, is that of the scientific education of girls. Nobody pointed out that it is intensified in some ways by the greater attention paid in girls' grammar schools to the aesthetic subjects which Miss Huxstep was unwilling to displace in favour of science. That attention is not unrelated to prospects of marriage and motherhood which dominate girls' education. Even in the girls' schools, however, the number taking science in G.C.E. examinations has been increasing steadily. If special steps are not taken the increase will soon be checked by the present acute shortage of women teachers. The girls are in more danger than the boys.

It is said that the reluctance of industry to employ trained women is preventing girls from taking science courses, but in fact industrial demand is one of the factors which are making women science teachers relatively scarcer than men. So in one sense the women's problem is not greatly different from that of men, and the solution may be the same, that is to check temporarily the flow of women to industry until the teacher shortage has been made good.

If the foregoing problems were disposed of, there would still remain what may be called the educator's own unfinished business. Sir Eric James's programme of science for the non-scientists has carried the debate on that subject a stage further; his colleagues will now continue to discuss whether his plan is suitable for those not in the highest ranges of ability. He will no doubt hold his own in this field, but there ought to be some examination of lower and middle school curricula if there is to be science for all in forms below the sixth. Some consideration should be given to current discontent with what is taught under the title of general science. It may be that general science is one of those subjects which can be handled only by exceptionally gifted teachers, who are not found in every school. Or perhaps elementary biology and the subject known as physics-with-chemistry should be taught as separate subjects to most pupils in the time now available for middle school science.

Lower still in the age range comes primary school science. The Conference was told that it ought to be more than 'just one

149

period a week of nature study'. But there was also a warning against the alleged danger of attempting systematic physical science too soon. Efforts are needed to reconcile these points of view. Somewhere between them is probably one which will provide young children with satisfying, if not final, answers to their important questions and dispose them towards quantitative and systematic approaches at a later stage.

The influences which do affect pupils' minds when the time for specialization comes are of great importance. Some members of the Conference may have hoped for discussion of the forces which attract or repel able pupils at this time. Even this Conference would not have wished all to become scientists. We were not told how the abler pupils distribute themselves in their sixth-form studies, but, in spite of recent trends, science probably gets rather less than its fair share of them. Tradition, scholarships and the influence of teachers all play their part in producing this effect, and they can all be allowed for. But what is to be done when able boys and girls of seventeen recoil from science because they think it is inhuman, and uninspired? They see its activities mainly in terms of bombs and missiles, and they suspect scientists of being unimaginative and unsympathetic where questions of goodness and beauty are involved. Perhaps most of these pupils should be guided to arts subjects anyway; but it will be a great pity if science does not attract some of them by its promise of virtue in the service of their fellow men, and of exhilaration in conceiving and reaching new stages in the mastery of nature and the knowledge of life. So we come back to Sir Eric James's thesis of science as a component of general education, with the modification that it is not only a sixth-form problem, but one affecting the whole educational field.

150